JIMMY SQUIB'S
GUIDE TO
HOW TO LIVE WITH HORSES
AND NOT GO
BARMY

By

Richard Westwood-Brookes

Drawings by

Kirk Wyton

This work is entirely fictional. The characters and situations in this book are entirely imaginary and bear no relation to any real person either living or dead, nor any actual happening, and no inference should be construed nor implied that any quoted names or events relate to any real person either living or dead. Any resemblance to real persons living or dead is purely coincidental.

Published in 1998 by Richard Westwood-Brookes
The Old Post Office
Ashford, Carbonell
Ludlow, Shropshire
SY8 4DB

Typeset and printed by
Aldine Press
Barnards Green Road
Malvern, Worcestershire
WR14 3BN

ISBN 0 9534670 0 7

DEDICATION

To Julie, Amie, Lucy, Wills and Justin – my special people

And Henry and Zak– two remarkably barmy horses without whose
help this would never have happened.

A practical guide to survival for every non horsey person
which will allow you to keep most of your
marbles, conkers and anatomy intact.

KIRK WYTON has been interested in cartooning all of his life. He practiced as a child drawing characters from American comic books and British cartoon strips like 'The Beano', but his influences range from everything from Walt Disney to Gerald Scarfe. His other interests include martial arts, football and Star Trek. He has three children and lives with his partner in Oswestry, Shropshire.

INTRODUCTION

This little guide is intended for all those people, like me, who have found themselves in a rather strange situation in their human relationships.

What started out as a seemingly good idea – i.e. a relationship with another human being involving all those usual things you do with another person, like going to the theatre, having parties, watching the telly, eating, sleeping, and having the occasional dabble at the old rumpy-pumpy – has now turned out, by some strange stealth which seemed to have crept up on you unawares to be a sort of a *menage à trois* in which hardly any of these things seem to take place any more.

Instead, the world seems to be full of wellies, smelly cardigans, standing out on damp fields, with the rain coming down about your ears. And muck. Tons and tons of muck. Muck on your hands, muck in your hair, muck on the best outfit which you promised yourself you would wear when you went out for the evening to that swanky restaurant you had always promised yourself you were going to go to when it was your birthday, but found out that on the way there was going to be a little detour which involved even more muck than usual.

And what, you may ask, has brought about this state of affairs? This bedlam on earth? This mind numbing, alcoholism inducing, bash-your-head-against-the-nearest-brick-wall-take-me-to-the-nearest-funny-farm-for-intensive-one-to-one-therapy-inducing-hysterical-state-of-mind way of life?

Well. It's got four legs, a mane, two pointed ears, a strange looking brush of a tail, it costs a second mortgage to keep, is often called some sort of stupid name like 'Percy Pickwick III' or 'Archy's Arch Skulduggery V' [the number after the name is all important, but we'll come on to that later] it hates you to distraction and it has the sort of relationship with your partner which, if it were human, would have lawyers licking their sticky little money grabbing fingers with a vengeance.

But unfortunately for them [and, incidentally, for *you*], it's *not* human. It is, in fact *superhuman*. Far more human than you will ever be because it commands the level of affection from your partner which is so far above that which you manage to achieve as to be the difference between the relative heights of, say, the Ganges Delta and the summit of Everest.

In short:

IT'S YOUR PARTNER'S HORSE

And you can't get rid of it. And at the same time you don't want to walk out on your partner. So you're stuck. Stuck there, right in tons and tons of muck, wondering what to do with the rest of your life – which begins tomorrow and which might last you another 100 years for all you know.

So this little guide is intended to be your passport through the rest of your life. Your means of coping through the long days which are ahead and surviving with most of you sanity intact.

HOW YOU GOT INTO THIS MESS IN THE FIRST PLACE

Every guide has to start somewhere, so let's get started at the logical beginning, and discuss you and your partner – and of course the horse.

First of all, being a man, obviously I have had to write this rubbish [sorry, I mean this incredibly important literary masterpiece which is moreover a seminally quintessential existential microcosm for post Jimi Henrixian mankind as we enter the new millenium] from a male perspective. I make no apologies for this as in the main men seem to be the ones left on the periphery of the horsey world. Those who are in it adopt very specific roles, but we will come to that as we go along.

So I'm sorry if any of this might seem to any ultra feminist out there as something which you might term 'sexist'. I can assure you that it is not. Sex doesn't come into it. Horses see to that.

So if this is 'ist' at all, I suppose it could be termed 'horse-ist' – but as horses hate both horsey and non horsey people with the same relish, why should I care about their feelings?

So, moving on, we shall examine the first golden rule of the horsey world – the overall guiding principle so to speak, the first empirical law of the horse world, and one which you must always bear in mind [and it will help you on many many occasion as you quest for survival in life, I can assure you]. Stated simply enough, it is this:

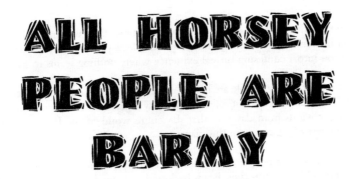

7

If this is indeed the case [and I can assure you beyond any question of a doubt that it is] then, if you are shacked up with a horsey partner, it must also follow that :

YOUR
PARTNER
IS
ALSO
BARMY

As long as you keep those two basic facts in mind at all times then you are well set for survival. Any deviation in thinking from this primary law may lead you into serious trouble, and will certainly lead you into a confusing surreal existence where nothing seems to make any sense.

Knowing now that all horsey people are barmy makes everything you encounter along the way eminently understandable, because it follows that every aspect of the horsey world is barmy too. So it is patently obvious from day one that the entire world of the horse operates counter clockwise to the rest of existence on this planet.

On occasions, even horsey people acknowledge that they are barmy. If you confront them with the fact they will often toss their heads back with a manic laugh, titter gleefully, then nod incessantly, often spluttering out: 'Yes we are ! Yes we are!' in a manner which also presupposes the unspoken rejoinder: 'And there's not a single thing on this planet that is going to be able to do anything about it.   So tough luck sucker !!'

So having understood that your partner is basically, well, **barmy,** you can then begin to come to terms with the relationship you have. So in the spirit of true counselling, [you know – where they always take you back through hypnosis until they find out that your problem was that when you were a child you really wanted to grow up to be a penguin] let's go back through those jolly old mists of time, shall we, to see where this sorry state of affairs first began – those heady days when you first met your partner.

They might seem a little far off now. So much has happened to change your life – the bouts of deep depression, the anxieties, reverse stress syndrome [whatever *that* is!] the nervous twitches, all those pills, self inflicted short term amnesia [the block of wood swiftly applied to the right temple proved the most effective, remember? – or come to think of it, you probably don't] and of course the draught pints of Scotch which you wished after a while could be obtainable in intravenous drip form on the NHS.

It might be a period which you had thought you could blot from your memory – but I'm afraid, as with many things we shall discuss in this little guide, you managed to fail quite spectacularly.

So cast your mind back to that fateful day, when you gazed starry eyed across the dinner table in that radiant, romantic atmosphere of that little downtown hideaway restaurant you had always promised yourself for that *really special* once-in-a-lifetime occasion [remember how you saved for **weeks and weeks** – did they really charge **THAT MUCH** for that dish which had one of those poncey sounding French cuisine sounding names, but turned out to be little more than scampi and chips!!!!] how you gushed with pride as you sipped that special toast in the *finest* Lambrusco to 'Us and Eternity' and all that sort of stuff, and the gypsy violinist bloke at your table intoned the gypsy waiter violinist version of 'She loves you yeah, yeah, yeah...'

Remember as you reached out to grab the hand from the other side of the table and gazed into the limpid pools of her eyes dreamily gazing back at you, how they suddenly narrowed and darkened, and a voice dreamily sounded as though in the very heavens above you:

'Dodo will be *so* pleased...'

Remember how you found your own eyes narrowing uncomfortably and you heard another voice which you suddenly recognised as your own saying:

'Dodo? Who's Dodo?'

Remember the warmth of her hand tightening its grip on yours.

'The **love of my life** silly!'

Remember the falter in your voice as you struggled with a rather ridiculous smirk on your face [why oh why is it that everyone *laughs* at times like this when your insides are churning up like a concrete mixer and that awful stab of adrenaline in the chest should really be inducing you to **scream**??? Still, that's not really a consideration for this volume, so we shall continue.]

'The . . . *love*? of your *life*? But . . . *I thought* . . . *I hoped* . . . *I DREAMED* . . . that it was *ME!!!*'

Remember the matter-of-fact way she looked into the candlelight?

'Well . . . *yes* . . . it *is* you Jimmy. . . but if you want me for your *very own*, you have to understand that the *real love of my life* is Dodo. *We are simply inseparable.*

There was a curious finality to that last remark. Laced with foreboding.

'Inseparable?'

'Yes. Inseparable. We've been together now for *ten years.* Even *you* couldn't make me give him up. *DON'T* say you'll *EVEN TRY'*

By now the grip on your hand was becoming rather vice-like if you recall.

Remember how you tried to maintain your composure – still with that awfully silly grin on your face, as you said:

'But who is this chap – French I suppose?'

'No. Irish Draft.'

'Irish Daft?'

'No. Irish **Draft** . . . Cross Thoroughbred.'

Remember how pennies were beginning to drop and a false sense of relief started to dispel the effects of the adrenaline.

'Oh, you said with a sigh. 'Dodo's your *horse!!!*'

'Yes, SILLY! What did you THINK I was on about?' she replied in a manner not out of place in the Bunty.

Remember how at that point, the vice was released on your hand and you desperately attempted to sooth the stabbing pains in your fingers while still trying to maintain your newly restored sense of equilibrium [and look kinda kool – huh?] the crumpled photograph was withdrawn and passed with an imperceptible loving caress across the table for your inspection.

'There he is – **MY BOY!!!** Aloisius Archibald Eric Pixilated Penguin III – but of course he'll *always* be **DODO** to me'

At this point you will have a memory which all the pills and alcohol could never allow you to blot out.

You actually took the picture, looked at it, and in your confused state of euphoria, relief, anger and elation, you actually said **[YES YOU DID, YOU ACTUALLY DID YOU DICKHEAD!!!!!!]**:

'What a lovely looking chap.'

THAT was the moment you did it. That was the moment when you formally entered the wonderful world of horses. That was the moment you turned your back on everything you had ever known up to that point and abandoned it for good.

Remember how you were never even given a second chance? How the picture was grabbed from your grasp in a whirlwind of excitement and how the person opposite dissolved into wild elation:

'Oh, I'm so PLEASED. So VERY VERY PLEASED, Jimmy, darling, Jimmy... I love you. Oh Jimmy, we're going to be so HAPPY, the three of us... SO HAPPY. You MUST see him... I know... *let's go an see him now... on the way home*... oh PLEASE PLEASE *PLEASE, IT WILL BE SO WONDERFUL...*'

As you hurriedly paid the bill, did you detect how the gypsy violinist bloke was playing something akin to a jazzed up gypsy violinist bloke version of 'What kind of fool am I' in his own excitement?

Remember, then, as you motored along uncertain lanes and byways to the accompaniment of the gushing blubberings of your by now ecstatic partner, a creeping unease started to take its toll of your whole body? Infesting its every portal. Insinuating its evil foreboding into every nook and cranny? And how you know that it's still there with you right now – like a latent virus, eating away at your brain every time you allow your mind to relax even for a micro second.

Remember how that unease grew to a sudden and shuddering overpowering ache as you approached a remote field gate far from civilisation and the nearest human being who could at least attempt to throw you a desperate lifeline, and your excited partner declared with that subtle combination of irony and sado-masochistic fulfilment that you have now come to recognise so well: 'WE'RE HERE'

Remember that moment? As you got out of the car, your partner had hitched up her tight cocktail skirt and vault fireman fashion over the five bars and then with no thought of the gold strapped sandals she had on her feet, she bounded with gay abandon through the mud with a 'Famous Five' 'COME ON JIMMY!!!' holler toward a bulky object dimly observable in the gathering twilight some distance across the field.

As you more gingerly negotiated the five bars, paying more attention to the effect it was having in terms of some sort of green slime being transferred in ever increasing quantities to the sleeves and legs of your best suit, your spirits sank as your best shoes, bought only that very morning for the occasion, you had in your naivety believed would be a romantic idyll at the restaurant and then [if best had come to best] a more extended sojourn between the sheets, sank into the oozing dankness of an impenetrable ocean of mud as thick and as uncompromising as caramel.

Then, in this impossibility, you became aware of the bulky object you had dimly observed, moving towards you with the same inevitability of gradualness with which the moon blots out the sun during a total eclipse – though with the supreme difference that in the astronomical situation, the moon finally moves on and it become daylight once more.

Then, after a few moments, there it was:

Aloisius Archibald Eric Pixilated Penguin III.

Here, at last was the creature from the oozing lagoon. This then was

standing there before you, eyeing you with an intense mixture of hatred, envy, loathing and contempt.

'Dodo . . . *this* is Jimmy . . . Jimmy Squib . . . we're all going to be so **HAPPY** together,' gushed your partner.

You, meanwhile, stood transfixed, mesmerised. Unable to move your feet, on account of the mud and unable to move your mind on account of the intensity of Dodo's transfixing stare.

You were revived somewhat by the urgency of your partner's command.

'Well, *aren't you going to say hello, Jimmy?'*

Her voice had curiously taken on a new inflexion never heard by you before you seem to recall. One of command. One of disappointment. That you had somehow not quite come up to her high expectations of you. One which you recognise daily these days.

Your Negative Account was opened at that moment, followed very rapidly by your second negative point when you made your first stupid remark.

Remember saying it? Remember saying: 'What on earth do I do?'

Remember the swift and derogatory reply:

'Give him a pat, stupid – here on the side of his neck . . . you don't know much about horses, do you?'

Remember doing as you were bidden.

Remember how Dodo froze for a second as you pathetically tried to carry out the instruction, as if the mere touch of your hand was such anathema to him that he felt in that moment that he needed intensive counselling of his own to relieve the stress of the invasion of his very existence?

Remember how, in one deft move, he turned his head towards you, took a large bite out of your jacket, then nudged you to the floor where you lay absorbing the muddy waters of a puddle?

Remember the glee of your partner as she burst out laughing at your predicament and enthused: 'Oh he LIKES YOU.   I KNOW that we are ALL going to be SO happy together – the three of us . . .'

Oh, happy memories!!!

⇒ MY NAME IS <u>NOT</u> ALOISIUS ARCHIBALD ERIC THE III ⇐

SOME INTERESTING ASPECTS OF THE HORSEY WORLD

We have now dealt with the very sad and sorry tale of how you found yourself in the mess you are in. I'm truly sorry for you, as a fellow sufferer, but sympathy and general understanding of your plight does nothing in terms of helping you to survive, bearing in mind that the mere fact that you are reading this little guide in the first place means that you are truly at the end of your tether.

So we shall press on being as positive as we can, and the next logical port of call will be to discuss the various truly interesting aspects of the horsey world.

Those more astute amongst you will no doubt draw your own conclusions over the word 'interesting' in this context – considering that someone once said that the worst thing you could ever say about anyone was that they were, well, interesting.

Anyway, the first consideration that we must, er, consider is this *vital question:*

THERAPY – CAN IT HELP?

Very shortly after entering the horsey world, you may erroneously think that seeking therapy might be the universal panacea to all your ills.

I am afraid that this would simply be a vast waste of time and money and deflect you from the urgent business of survival as best you can – and to this end I must be firm and unequivocal in my advice that you must **NOT EVEN CONSIDER IT.**

Let's look at it as rationally as we can, shall we?

As we have already established, **all horsey people are barmy.**

Given that this is the case, then, if you chose to go to seek therapy and you see that tell-tale picture or calendar, featuring one of our four legged friends, on the therapist's wall, then the chances are pretty high that your therapist is a horsey person, and therefore your therapist is **barmy** and probably needs **therapy.**

If, on the other hand, you seek therapy from a therapist who *doesn't* appear to have that tell tale picture on the wall, and *doesn't* respond when you pose a few well planned and probing questions such as: 'I wonder how high your wall is – 16.2, wouldn't you say?' or 'Didn't we meet at the Chatterley Witney in Hand Around the Houses Up Yours Dressage Racing Hunter Trials?', then, although you've probably found a therapist who is *not* horsey, and therefore probably *not* barmy, your therapist won't *understand* a word of what you are talking about, probably think that he has an out-and-out *nutter* on his hands and promptly have you committed.

The only glimmer of hope that you might have is to hit on a therapist who is non horsey, but *married* or somehow otherwise banged up with a horsey other half.

In this situation, you will have found, rather like finding that proverbial needle in a haystack, a *non* barmy therapist who is non horsey, and, *because* he or she is in a relationship with a horsey person, will totally understand both *what* you are *saying* and *what* you are *going through* and will therefore be fully conversant with the desperation which drove you to seek help in the first place, and will therefore not be surreptitiously reaching under the desk for the concealed alarm button which is on line directly to the boys in white coats.

I'm sorry to sound a bit of a downer here, but I'm afraid that the euphoria which you might be feeling at such a moment will be very short lived. You see, unfortunately, because of these very circumstances, your therapist will be totally useless to you, because he or she will be in **exactly the same mess as you** and while he/she might add to your list of desperate non horsey suffering friends and acquaintances and therefore make quite a convivial companion as you swap anecdotes about muck, as far as your mental well-being is concerned, he/she will be of no practical value whatsoever.

You're in it on you own, I am afraid. This one, you've got to work through yourself.

SOME CULINARY CONSIDERATIONS

Talking of fending for yourself, pretty soon into your relationship with your partner, you will come to realise one very important fact:

IF YOU ARE EVER GOING TO EAT AGAIN
YOU WILL HAVE TO LEARN
TO COOK FOR YOURSELF

It's not that your partner *can't* cook. Indeed you get the impression that somewhere along the line she learned to prepare meals pretty well – certainly judging by what she does every day for Dodo. But here lies the key. It's the fact that she's *far too busy* preparing the sumptuous repasts for Dodo that she simply hasn't any time left in her madcap horsey lifestyle to do anything for the likes of *you*.

Those more astute amongst you will learn this lesson very early on. By about day three, you will come to realise that those half empty bags of all sorts of milled, drilled, dried and fried foods of the most exotic kinds which you had originally thought were some sort of basic ingredients for who-knows-what culinary delights awaiting *you*, are not *exactly* what you thought they were. And come to think about it, you couldn't *exactly* remember eating anything at all, these past few days.

Whereas you had thought that when your partner retired to the kitchen to prepare the special little candlelight supper you were expecting, she didn't *actually* emerge for some two hours. And when she did, she was dressed in regulation jods and wellies and simply muttered something indistinguishable which definitely contained the words *field, Dodo and feed.*

When she re-emerged 45 minutes or so later, you may remember quizzing her about what was for supper, only to be told that she had already eaten and taken care of feeds for that night.

By this time, you realised that this had gone on for three nights running, and you were beginning to get decidedly peckish.

As I say, this is only a word of warning, because not all of you out there are necessarily astute enough to realise this and could go for *weeks* without food. Even less of you will be bold enough to investigate what is actually going on in the kitchen at such times.

If you are, then you will be treated to a nightly ritual, as dazzling as any druidic ceremony at Stonehenge on the solstice. As you gingerly peep around the crack in the kitchen door, trying as best you can to remain concealed, you will be confronted by your partner waltzing around the kitchen, brandishing a wooden spoon in one hand and a boiling hot kettle in the other. At her feet will be several buckets into which she will spoon various combinations of powder and granules from the aforementioned bags.

At this point, the most astute of you will begin to realise that the bags of what you thought said *'food'* on the labels actually say *'feed'* – which is, of course, something rather different to what you had in mind, both in terms of what it actually *is* and *who* it is intended for.

Once having completed the kitchen ritual, your partner will then don wellies and exit without any further ado, leaving the kitchen empty and inviting you to make a cursory inspection of the cupboards, shelves, fridge and freezer.

It is about now, if you have followed this pattern of behaviour to the letter, that you will begin to realise that apart from the various packages which you now see are marked clearly 'For Horses' and the odd mouldering crust and suspect smelling bottle of something indistinguishable bearing labels which indicate a sell-by date of some years ago, that there doesn't appear to be much in the way of anything which would vaguely be described as *'sustaining'* in the human sense.

You will now begin to suspect that the guy who ran Colditz was probably an ex-cavalry man, but don't waste time in such contemplation, because you have work to do – and fast!

It's vitally important that you learn this lesson very early on, or you may waste away as some emaciated cretin long before you can summon up the mental energy to read a cookbook.

Not all of you will achieve a perfect solution, I have to say. Some may have to settle for that rather unsettling *middle solution* which will mean the influx of rather alarming piles of tins of **baked beans** into your life.

For those of you in this state: **HERE'S A TIP!!!**

Somewhere in the kitchen [just to confirm: that's the room that has a sink in it, even though it doesn't look much like what you think a kitchen *should* look like, with all the feed troughs and buckets and bags etc strewn all over the place – but *don't* confuse it with the one that has the bog in it as well – that's the *bathroom* remember] you should find a round metal object with a straight handle attached to it. This is called a *'sauce-pan'*.

If you then open your next can of baked beans, and empty the contents into the *'sauce-pan'* and then put the *'sauce-pan'* on to a lit gas ring or electric element which has been turned to the 'on' position, and leave it for a few minutes, the baked beans will become hot. You will almost certainly enjoy hot baked beans far more than the cold variety you have hitherto been eating straight from the can.

HERE'S ANOTHER TIP!!!

When you've finished, why not swill the *'sauce-pan'* as well as your plate under the running tap at the sink. That way they will be **washed** so you will be able to use them again and again and you won't have to keep on buying dozens and dozens of *'sauce- pans'* and plates which could prove expensive and moreover unnecessarily divert vital funds away from much more important areas of expenditure – like horses.

Many of you will have made that enormous leap for mankind and realised that beyond the 14th day without adequate food, the average bloke starts to go down hill fast and decided that in all honesty something practical should be done about it.

Some of you will of course have long settled for a regular diet of takeaways, convenience and junk food. While this is not a totally adequate solution such a regime is at least a bit more filling than an incessant diet of cold baked beans, while others will have been super successful and dragged some dim distant memory of cooking beans in the way I have just described from some portal of their brains and applied this knowledge immediately. They will then have at least a nourishing foundation upon which they can build.

And I have to say that some non-horsey other halves become remarkably successful in their culinary achievements, moving on from beans to chips, to steak and then, from there to untold heights.

You can easily identify such blokes when you go down the pub. They're the ones who seem to have the mild, well adjusted **well fed** demeanour, as opposed to the hot beans and fish and chips brigade who have that rather ruddy, slightly oily, slightly **overstuffed** complexion – and of course the totally hopeless cases who seem to be wasting away before your very eyes, but who still seem to take some sort of perverse pride in declaring that 'cold baked beans are the best food in the world' and will even defend this view as a couple of colleagues begin to heap praise over their mutual efforts in producing the most delectable 'Quennells de Quaille avec Jus de Frambois' followed by the most heavenly 'Soufflé d'Orange au mouse de chocolate', and a couple of others start discussing the merits of the saveloy at 'Greasy Joe's Fishbar' and whether its better than the Balti Pies from Abdul's chippery.

It's pathetic, I know, to hear these desperate, wan, lonely men trying to sound macho by declaring that ' nothing is going to get me from a can of good old cold baked beans', but if you are one of the 'Caviar and Canapés' or 'Fishbar and Balti' brigades, please *do* try your best to bring such people into the fold – even if it's only to introduce them to the whereabouts of the kitchen and the existence of the aforementioned *'sauce-pan'*. It *could* be lifesaving.

But I know in all this discussion about food, one rather important question is still lingering in the back of your mind and it would be wrong of me not to ask it on your behalf.

What, you are thinking, happens to your horsey other half in all of this? *What* will be sustaining *her?*

The answer to that one is simple.

First of all, she will know about heating up baked beans – it's something women seem to be *born* with.

Second she will have developed a particular liking for Country Mix and Bran Mash [don't worry too much about what *these* are, just suffice it to say that as you're not horsey, you won't like them and anyway it would be more than your life's worth to be discovered trying the odd spoonful, as they're **strictly reserved** for **Dodo** – understand?].

Thirdly – and this applies particularly if you have developed a culinary talent – she will stuff herself legless on your cooking.

THE LANGUAGE – WHAT ON EARTH DOES IT ALL MEAN?

The next most important thing to remember – and keep this consoling thought with you at all times, as a kind of stabilising foundation, a very talisman of your existence – is that:

YOU ARE *DEFINITELY NOT* BARMY

even though at times you might feel that you are. This is especially at times when you are in horsey company and you realise that you don't understand a single word they are talking about.

At such times it is vital to remember that this is a perfectly logical state of affairs, and at the risk of repeating myself [but I need to drill this one home] YOU ARE *DEFINITELY NOT* BARMY.

The explanation is simple.

In order to protect themselves from certification, horsey people have invented their own language which seems to mean everything to them and which actually means nothing to you.

So, when in a horsey presence, you are immediately thwarted from summoning the boys in white coats because it is you who does not appear to be talking plain English – see?

Let me give you an example.

You might consider that your partner's horse [Dodo, remember . . . his *name's* Dodo] measures 6ft or so from the top of his back to the ground.

Not so.

Actually, you will be informed, he's a *16.2.*

[Of course he is, you will be thinking. *How stupid* of me not to realise *that!*]

What *that* means, actually is that he is just over *16 hands* high – or putting it another way, he is the height of sixteen hand palms laid next to each other up his leg to the top of his shoulder – right?

You may now be wondering in your abject ignorance, *who* in Christendom is going to get sixteen people to stand on top of each other in order to measure all this up correctly.

You may also be wondering how such a precise measurement as **16.2** can be achieved when everyone on the planet has different sized hands and **FOR GOD'S SAKE!!!** your own *right* hand is a different size to your *left* – it's the *nature* of human beings. To say nothing of the difference between the hand sizes of, say, a humungus lump hammer operator and a ballerina.

No matter. It is pointless trying to apply any *empirical science* to such things. All it will earn you is yet more negative points on your, by now, rather bulging tally, and your first real *disparaging remark:*

'*Any fool* can see he's a **16.2**. It's his *size* stupid.'

Further salt will be rubbed into the wound during general conversation when you will face the ridicule of a collection of horsey types such as:

[Your partner, probably doing something in keeping with the general air of sadism, like peeling the wings off a butterfly] 'Jimmy thinks Dodo *isn't* a 16.2'

This will be greeted by peels of laughter and the comforting and condescending touch of an all-knowing horsey elder who will say something like: 'Jimmy dear... **16.2** is Dodo's *size*. He couldn't *possibly* be anything else...' [It all becomes pretty clear now, doesn't it?]

They will then move on to talk voluminously about other meaningless terms, such as withers, hocks, fetlocks, 'he got a stone lodged in his frog the other day...' and so on and so forth.

During this conversation, the actual *names* of various horses will no doubt be discussed.

As we have seen, horses tend to have **two names** – the first is their **true name,** and almost without exception, it is the sort of name which, if given to you, would prompt you to first walk around with a bag over your head, and then emigrate.

No doubt horsey people realise that if their horses *knew* they had these names, *they* probably would too, so therefore *all* horses have another name, like Dodo for example.

This is the name under which the horse exists for most of the time – but it is obviously very important that it has a real name, and that that real name is long and ridiculous, because every now and then, the horsey person is required to enter the horse at an event under its *real* name, and by having a long, rambling, ridiculous sounding name, the horse *sounds* as though it belongs to the Gentry [of which more anon] and therefore the horsey person who owns it is, by inference, also vaguely associated with the Gentry, if only for that moment. We'll come on to *why* it is so important for the horsey person to be vaguely associated with the Gentry a little later on, but if, for the moment, we take this as fact, it becomes immediately clear why the number at the end of the name is so **vitally important.**

Calling the horse Ashington Abbots Rural Development Grant Aid III, **implies** that there *must have been* an Ashington Abbots Rural Development Grant Aid I and II – i.e. there is a *progeny* here. A *line*. A *bloodstock*.

The fact that there might *never* have been either of these two entities, nor the fact that the name actually came into that particular horsey person's head when she was sitting on the bog reading a pamphlet entitled 'Ashington Abbots Rural Development Grant Aid – The Way Forward' which was obtained by her partner when he was down at the Bank while desperately trying to negotiate the latest extension to his ever growing overdraft [on account of...well, I guess you are probably beginning to realise that *yourself* by now] really never comes into it. People in the horsey world never seem to question such things. They simply take them at face value, and sometimes might even *admire* the social standing of someone else if they happen to have a horse with a *particularly* long, complicated and *thoroughly downright stupid* name, suffixed, of course, with as high a number as they can reasonably get away with such as Canute Cathaginian Charlemagne Lucius Marcellus Marcus Tullius in Tablino Sedet Microdidinus of Thebes XXIII – 'but he'll *always* be *Bloater* to me'

It's rather like when you are at a party and some finger turns up in a Porsche. As he smoothes his way in an oily sort of fashion from the crushed leather upholstery, and deftly flicks his remote control locking beam, which is duly acknowledged by the car with a wink of the headlights – how many of the gorgeous girls falling at his feet wonder just *how* the car is financed? Not one, you suspect. It is just accepted that *he* somehow is *loaded* – a feeling which is endorsed by the muttered comment from some berk standing next to you who says something like: 'Old Barry's doing well for himself...' without ever allowing you to make reference to the fact that 'Barry' could have leased, rented, borrowed or even stolen the car, or he could be a garage mechanic and is merely taking the vehicle out for an extended road test while the real owner is back at base looking anxiously at his watch with increasing impatience.

But anyway – back to names.

It is as important in its own way that the *second* name of the horse is childish and silly.

Names like 'Dodo', 'Stinky', 'Winky', 'Woozy" etc abound because they *sound* like the sort of names that those crass bores who went to the right school call all their rugger mates, and who in later life turn out to be rather boringly High Court Judges, Chairmen of Water Utilities, *your* Bank Manager etc etc.

Anyway, enough of names, because before we move onto further aspects of the horse itself, there is another matter which is of vital importance, mainly because you can never, ever, get rid of it, and I cannot put off discussing it any longer.

I refer of course to

Muck is an integral and important part of the whole world of the horse – because it is erupting out of his rear end at almost every opportunity.

In goes the grass and all the other goodies with all sorts of strange sounding names like 'Country Mix' ' Bran Mash' etc etc which horsey people stuff down the one end, and then, *hey presto!* out of the *other* end comes muck. Tons of it. All over the place. All over the field. All over the yard. All over the road. All over the stable. All over the hay. All over the water buckets. All over the trough.

And of course – all over *you.*

There never seems to be a moment in the day when muck isn't being produced. Never a moment when the tail isn't in that ominous raised position, the head thrown back and the look of defiant glee glistening on the snorting nostrils as if the beast is declaring: 'Look at me, folks – I'm at it *again!*' and the air takes on that all too familiar sickly sweet smell and the harmony of birdsong and breeze is rudely punctuated by the percussion of piles plummeting to the ground.

Horsey people love muck. They revel in it. They spend many a waking hour in its company, tossing it about with gay abandon. What's more, the prospect of starting the day knee deep in

piles of the stuff seems to be the greatest motivation for getting up long before sunrise even in the height of summer.

As you zed peacefully away, dreaming of long forgotten days when a day out meant a trip to that idyllic half timbered and thatched country pub which serves up the best lobster thermidor around, and surrounded by people who regale you with anecdotal conversation about far away places where people lie in hammocks playing beaten up guitars and slurping pina coladas through straws – your partner has long left you for the pleasures of frollicking around in muck.

Most of the time you only ever know that this strange twilight world of muckfrollicking is taking place from circumstantial evidence – waking up as the sun plays gentle sarabands on your face to find that the space next to you in bed, which you were sure was occupied the night before by your partner, is now empty and quite cold; going downstairs to find evidence that coffee has been brewed, but so long ago that the kettle is only lukewarm; discovering, on investigation, that a pair of wellies is missing from the rack in the porch, and [and this is the clincher] the broom and the rake are missing as well.

On isolated occasions, usually when your peaceful slumbers are disturbed by a vague nightmare creeping into your mind, that your world has been invaded by this terrifying, snorting, four legged beast depositing muck all over the place, and your body's natural mental defences have dragged you away from this primeval horror and fitfully thrown you into some sort of waking limbo, your eyes will flicker open to see the receding form of your partner exiting from your room cloaked by the shroud of semi-darkness.

On enquiry as to where she is going, you will be informed in mumbled tones something about 'mucking out' – which means in translation into youspeak: 'I'm going to have a wonderful hour or so frollicking about in muck in the middle of the night, in pouring rain and in the freezing cold – and I'm going to *bloody well enjoy every minute...*'

On the face of it, being in this sort of state – your unconscious world swinging madly between unfulfilled promise of idyllic reveries and dark, satanic, muck-filled nightmares – and your waking life underpinned by the tragic reality that everything you had been confronted with in those nightmares was actually **very real** and **very true**, might be a recipe for disaster.

But you must understand that no one is going to suffer from this state of affairs other than you. So it is vitally important that you start pulling yourself together and start to get your own mind attuned to the way in which you can actually cope with this state of affairs.

In other words, it is high time that you started to:

DEVELOP A POSITIVE ATTITUDE TOWARDS MUCK

The first thing to bear in mind is that: **Muck is a very useful commodity.**

If you can get this firmly entrenched into your mind, then you are starting off very well indeed. In order to get you in the right frame of mind for this, we must consider, just *why* it *is* such a *very essential, useful* commodity.

I find the best way of doing this is to list its very useful, er, uses – if you see what I mean.

1. Once it has spent months rotting away in ever increasing smelly piles putrefying away and providing an ideal habitat for flies, wasps, and various worms, weevils and vermin, you can put it on your roses. I'm told it helps them to grow somewhat – with rather the same sort of results you can obtain from one of those cheap rose fertilisers you can get from Woolworth's.

2. That's it.

Now you will realise that out of the horse's rear end comes a valuable commodity. Nay, one which is *vital* to the nation's economy.
You can even let your imagination roam free for a while, as, with glee and gay abandon, you can enjoy the satisfaction of watching your partner's horse continue to do his own little bit for the nation. Day after day, hour after hour, minute by minute.

And suddenly, all those little nagging doubts that you had about those stained and ruined clothes and shoes, pale into insignificance when set alongside the importance of what your four legged friend is doing for the further development of this great nation of ours.

Good gracious, you suddenly realise – there are probably armies of commodity brokers in the City sweating blood over the stuff. The international wires are alive with the latest prices in muck. *Fortunes* are being made every minute. The Internet probably has *thousands* of websites devoted to it. There's a whole training industry for those involved with it. Marketing and advertising agencies are pitting their most creative professionals towards producing the ultimate campaign, and self made men are benignly turning to their favoured sons with the avuncular arm around the shoulder technique to inform them that they would not have got where they are today had it not been for their shrewd speculation in *Muck Futures.*

Suddenly, you discover that you are witnessing the same process which led to the BIRTH OF A NATION.

And it makes you feel proud. Proud that you are connected in your own small way with such an important, nay, *VITAL* operation.

THAT is what developing a positive attitude towards Muck is all about – though rest easy that you will not have to break your slumbers in order to join the early morning muckfrollickers. That particular activity is strictly reserved for the barmy.

THE HORSE

Now we move on to perhaps the most importantly interesting aspect of the whole interesting world of horses – I refer, of course, to the horse itself.

The first thing to remember [and *always* remember this] is that:

HORSES ARE DEFINITELY *NOT* BARMY

They are, in fact, **SADISTS** who achieve intense pleasure out of inflicting pain, suffering, and constant mental trauma on horsey people, who of course *ARE* barmy.

In other words, all horses indulge in the age-old medieval pastime of **Mocking the Afflicted.**

As a result of this, they **hate** non horsey people like you with a vengeance, because there is always the possible threat that one day their little game may be exposed and horsey people will see them for what they *really* are.

Any non horsey person could easily disabuse them of this belief of course by simply pointing out that congenitally barmy people **never** get better – but you're never going to succeed here, because congenitally sane but devious entities, like horses, will **never** believe you on the basis that you must be like them and therefore have some sort of perverse ulterior motive – like moving in on their patch with the idea of taking over as chief mocker of the afflicted and thus having your own fun. They would see you as having some sort of devious master plan such as having your partner [suitably chained up of course] performing a series of party tricks to the hilarity of your high class non horsey friends along the lines of ' go on Helen, fall off Dodo again in that funny way you did last week . . . ha ha ha' or ' . . . I say, everyone, Helen's going to talk in that stupid way all these barmy horsey people talk – go on Helen why don't you tell us *all about* a 16.2 . . . ha ha ha...we're all having such a great laugh at your expense . . . sorry everyone, that's all for today, because I've got to return Helen to the funny farm . . . ha ha ha'

Well, you ought to know by now that it doesn't *quite* work that way, and anyway you would have tremendous difficulty in persuading a horse otherwise, because **horses don't speak English** – or hadn't you noticed that one either?

What you **must** do is to make sure you always keep a respectful distance from horses at all times.

Any encroachment into the danger area will earn you a bite [as you already discovered on your first meeting] or a kick – which can be either *forwards:* this, by the way, is called a *'Cow Kick'* [don't bother to enquire why a kick from a horse is called a *'Cow Kick'* it's all part of the general barminess of the horse world and therefore within this context, *entirely* logical] or more probably from the **rear.** This is called a **Buck** and will always come when you least expect it – and if you receive one of these you will probably end up in the next field.

These are only two weapons in the considerable arsenal available to the average horse, however.

Sometimes, even when you are maintaining the respectful distance, you will not escape, because the horse, no doubt feeling that it is sometime since you had your fair share of punishment, will come to you. The first you will know of this is a nudge in the back which will send you flying to the floor. This is known as **herding you up,** and once again, as you try to dust off the gathering crusts of dirt and grime from your clothing, don't expect any sympathy or sanction from your partner

On the contrary, this will attract the amused giggle and the cuddle [for the *horse* of course, stupid!!] followed by the 'Oh, Dodo, you *do* love Jimmy, don't you – and mummy *loves* you, Dodo dearest . . .'

Dodo will cement this portion of your continuing and evolving relationship by standing on your foot. He will do this quite subtly. First of all, he will look quite docile and dopey as your partner goes into ever increasingly stupid levels of syrupy gushes, his lip will begin to droop and you might think that he is about to fall asleep.

Then, at that precise moment, as you are taken off your guard, dusting down the sleeves on your jacket, across will come the hoof which will ever so imperceptibly be placed on the end of your toes.

As you yelp in pain and hop about clutching the crushed toes and ruined footwear, your partner will first chastise you for 'startling Dodo' then remind you [as if you didn't know by now] that 'Dodo's such a biggly-wiggly boy' and you should have made sure your foot was out of the way.

The next thing to bear in mind about horses is that they are so desperate in their manic congenital sadism that they will sometimes indulge in self sacrifice in order to achieve maximum torture.

If there is a pot hole in the field, the horse will surely find it and fall down it.

If the field is bounded by barbed wire, the horse will inevitably walk into it, putting a good six inch gash in his head. Don't think you will get away lightly if there is a hedge, because he will simply get stuck in it – and in such a complicated way that it will almost always require the services of several local fire brigades to cut the bastard out.

But perhaps the most extreme example of this desperate catalogue of mental anguish infliction is

The Horse

This, quite simply, is a most distressing condition brought on by **eating grass.**

Now, you may in your naive stupidity think that **grass** is what horses tend to **live on.** A sort of **staple diet.**

Well – yes. It is. But it also causes laminitis which at its worst extremities, can kill them.

They obviously know that horsey people know that, and therefore laminitis causes the horsey people to have their worst nightmare.

So what do horses do? Yes, you've got it – they spend more and more of their time eating more and more grass. It's as simple as that – and pretty logical, I'm sure you will agree.

They get laminitis. The *horsey person* gets even barmier and spends a king's ransom on Vet's bills curing it. Then, when all this terrible torture time is terminated, and the ransom paid, the horse goes out and eats grass all over again. Cute hey?

But such behaviour is far from mad from the horse's point of view. Such self sacrifice achieves three main objectives:

1. It hardly gets ridden

2. It always enjoys a mega pampered existence

3. It always remains centre stage in your partner's affections – and *you* don't get a look in.

You, on the other hand, could never expect to be so fortunate. In the event of a similar calamity befalling you, like an impacted wisdom tooth, for example, the very best you can expect as you lie there 'twixt life and death, is the admonition that you should have gone to the dentist weeks ago – it's your own fault. Followed by: 'You'll have to look after yourself today, anyway. I've got to go down to the field and meet the Vet. Dodo's laminitis is no better...'

Laminitis is not the only self inflicted condition which horses self inflict on themselves to cause maximum damage to your relationship with your partner.

There are millions of them. There *have* to be, when you come to think of it. After all, the laminitis scam wouldn't work *every* day of the year.

So in between bouts of laminitis, there will be bouts of suspected colic, ringworm, botflies, tapeworm, flu, stable cough, even the effects of eating poisonous plants like bracken, and ragwort, which must taste dreadful to the average horse, but which he nevertheless gobbles with glee, thinking, no doubt, that by the morning, the onset of fever will ensure a confinement to stable for at least six weeks, lots of money being spent, even, perhaps, the ensured presence of

31

your partner *overnight* in the stable, keeping some sort of lonely vigil by his side. This is without doubt the best possible outcome, because this ensures that if *her* vigil is lonely, *you* will be even lonelier still.

Mention of this state of general disease, brings me of course to the next important topic – that of

the Vet

On the face of it, the Vet might seem your greatest ally. After all, **Vets make a certain proportion of their living out of shooting horses, don't they?**

Yes. This is certainly true, but remember that Vets also make a certain proportion of their living by shoving their arms up cows' backsides on a regular basis – so you must seriously consider whether it is worth the risk trying to make an ally of this person, or whether it is better to keep a similarly respectful distance away from him as you do with horses.

On paper, all Vets are billionaires. On paper they could afford to turn up to your field driving a Roller assigned to that particular day of the week. On paper any Vet could take over from the Queen tomorrow as the wealthiest person in the entire universe.

But in practice, the average Vet will turn up to your place driving a beaten up old station wagon and wearing cavalry twill, brown brogues [specially selected for their hardwearing longevity] and a faded sports jacket with those tell-tale leather patches at the elbow which teachers and social workers wear.

There is a very good reason for this.

HORSEY PEOPLE NEVER PAY THEM

or at least hardly ever do. The enormous fees which the Vets charge and which would lead the averagely naive person to believe, like the aforementioned fingers you meet at parties that: '. . . the Vet must be doing bloody well . . .' are unfortunately for Vets **never paid** by due date and more often than not are dumped into what is often termed the

𝕽unning 𝕱arm 𝕬ccount

It's called that for obvious reasons, because the other major potential source of income, i.e. farmers, don't pay Vets either. They too have 𝕽unning 𝕱arm 𝕬ccounts, which means that if, in say January, the Vet is called out in the middle of a blizzard at 2am in order to stick his arm up a cow's arse, he will finally get paid for his time and trouble in February – some years later.

Horsey people are even worse than this. Some **Running Farm Accounts,** I believe commenced during the reign of Charles II, and have yet to be cleared. Accounts begun before the reign of the Merry Monarch [and there were thousands] were cunningly torn up during the Civil War and the Vets who issued them denounced as traitors to the Commonwealth and promptly dispatched to the Tower.

In fact, I believe there is a very cogent theory gaining an ever widespread acceptability in academic circles that the very *reason* for the Civil War was so that thousands of horsey people who had by that time fallen so desperately behind in the repayment of their **Running Farm Accounts** which had been steadily accumulating since the previous big upheaval – during the Wars of the Roses some 200 years previously – could legitimately forget about them and start afresh.

If you don't subscribe to this theory, then ask yourself these two questions: Why did so many horses seem to have been involved in the Civil War? And why were the most decisive battles fought by the *cavalry,* led in the main by hyper barmy horsey types, like Prince Rupert, who, even in those times was recognised as the 'Mad' Cavalier????

Similarly, you can see the shadowy presence of the **Running Farm Account** behind many a subsequent event in history. Furthermore, closer study of the documentary evidence clearly shows a pattern emerging and one is led to speculate whether one of the greatest hitherto undiscovered elements in the shaping of this nation is the fact that the horsey fraternity, having scored such a spectacular clearing of the slate through their behind-the-scenes sponsorship of Oliver Cromwell, were bidding to achieve a much more formalised and *regular* emptying of the **Running Farm Accounts.**

Unfortunately for them, they obviously chose the wrong blokes to further their cause. Instead of achieving the desired result, Monmouth's Rebellion of 1685 petered out at Sedgemoor [another cavalry charge by the way] and the subsequent efforts of James II in 1690 and his son James Francis Edward Stuart in 1715 similarly foundered.

James's son, the ignominious 'Bonnie' Prince Charlie who was basically Italian and hardly spoke a word of English almost gave the game away when he concluded with his hot Latin temperament that enough had been endured by his British horsey mates who by that time were getting so hopelessly behind in settling their **Running Farm Accounts** that bailiffs were beginning to be called in. He therefore decided to confront the issue head on and embarked on a regional tour of Scotland and various places in the north of England between 1745 and 1746 promoting what he thought was the horsey cause.

Unfortunately, being a Johnny foreigner, what he thought was the English for 'let's bury the **Running Farm Account** for good' came out sounding something like 'I call upon my fellow Scots to rise up against the tyrannical English' with disastrous results, both for the Scots, who erroneously thought this Italianate creep was one of them, and for the horsey fraternity in general who had to wait until Napoleon came on the scene some 50 years later to have any chance of getting financially straight again. Unfortunately even then, their efforts did not bring in particularly spectacular results, as a good deal of the Napoleonic Wars were fought on the sea by that Nelson chap, who although he *looked* like he might be a mega-horse buff with his one arm and one peeper [we'll deal with horse inflicted injuries later on] was in reality a jolly jack tar who was definitely *not* that way inclined [nor *that* way, I would guess, unless you believe all that 'kiss me Hardy' stuff].

I have a niggling feeling that perhaps it was the Vets, who, after suffering the debacle of the Civil War got their act together and decided that from thereon there would *never again* be a civil strife which would permit the horsey fraternity to tear up their 𝕽unning 𝕱arm 𝕬ccounts. More research needs to be done, I feel, on the financial aspects of the backing which James II received in 1685 [he appears to have changed sides a couple of years later, by the way, when he turned Catholic, and was presumably promised something pretty special by the horsey people], William III received in 1690, George I received in 1715 and George II received in 1745/6.

I wouldn't be at all surprised if the finance wasn't provided by some shadowy society known as 'The Eternal Anti-Equestrian Secret Brotherhood of Vets', or something like that.

Anyway, whatever the explanation, the 𝕽unning 𝕱arm 𝕬ccount is still very much a reality, which means that whenever the Vet calls – and it's usually *once a week* – what with laminitis, colic, stable cough etc etc etc, you **MUST** ensure that you make yourself scarce.

I cannot stress how **ABSOLUTELY VITAL** this is for your general well-being and your finances.

You see, if horses have been running in your partner's family for generations, there is every possibility that the 𝕽unning 𝕱arm 𝕬ccount could be as much as **THREE HUNDRED YEARS OLD**. Even if horses have only recently come into your partner's life, there is every possibility that her 𝕽unning 𝕱arm 𝕬ccount could be up to 10 years old.

Which means that if you appear on the scene, as a perceived non horsey person who has the possibility of having access to some funds, you will be *seized* upon by the Vet as the one and only God given chance he has had in a lifetime to clear your partner's 𝕽unning 𝕱arm 𝕬ccount in *one fell swoop.*

In this instance you will be standing there, having been induced by your partner into some sort of ridiculous activity like holding on to Dodo while the Vet gives him his latest anti laminitis booster injection.

She will be saying something like: 'It doesn't seem to be having much of an effect on him, Mr Vet.'

He, meanwhile, will be thinking: ' No, Helen. An injection of coloured water won't have any effect on him whatsoever, but as I'm not going to get paid for it anyway because you will no doubt ask me to add this to the 𝕽𝖚𝖓𝖓𝖎𝖓𝖌 𝕵𝖆𝖗𝖒 𝕬𝖈𝖈𝖔𝖚𝖓𝖙, why should I bother using *real* medicines. And anyway the pratt is perfectly healthy, if you weren't so congenitally barmy you'd realise that Dodo is only winding you up to get more affection, but you won't listen to any rational argument because you're barmy, so why should I care?'

But what he will *actually* say will be something like: 'Don't worry, Helen. He will be as right as rain in a few days. All that it will take will be a few more injections, some follow up visits, and then several night time vigils when you can monitor the situation over, say, a four hour intensive monitoring period and then I'm sure everything will be well.'

At that point he will remember you standing there like a spare part, trying desperately to come to terms with just what you are doing there and to look invisible.

You will know you are heading for trouble if he gives a shifty look towards the rusting patches on the beaten up old shooting brake he turned up in, and then wipes his brow with the threadbare sleeve of his well worn sports jacket.

He will then ask you a vital and probing question: ' Are *you* into horses, Mr Squib?'

You will no doubt fail to answer at this point, not knowing the purpose of this exercise. Your stalling will be to little avail, however, because your partner will very kindly speak on your behalf:

' No... he tries *very hard* but I'm afraid that Jimmy just doesn't seem to be interested . . . it's all very sad, really. . . '

At that point an evil little grin will come over the Vet's face and then he will turn to your partner and say something like: 'I particularly need the Reverse Thrust Hacking Untoward Zimbabwean Bit, please Helen [we'll go into what on earth *this* means a bit later on, by the way] Could you get it for me?'

At his urgent bidding, your partner will then leave you alone and stranded in this field with a vampirical Vet about to suck your blood.

He will then turn to you slowly and say in an equally slow and ponderous sort of voice which contains very deliberately chosen words and inflections:

'There's a small matter of the 𝕽𝖚𝖓𝖓𝖎𝖓𝖌 𝕵𝖆𝖗𝖒 𝕬𝖈𝖈𝖔𝖚𝖓𝖙, Mr Squib, which needs settling up before I can do any more. I didn't like to speak in front of Helen, in case it was too *embarrassing* – but could you possibly see your way to . . .'

At that point he will jab the needle he has been holding in his hand for the last ten minutes into Dodo's rump and Dodo, for his part will obligingly react by standing on your foot again, to which you will yell out:

'Aghhhhhhhhhhhhhhhhhhhhhhhhh!!!!!!'
which, to your horror, you will suddenly realise sounded rather too much like:

'Yeahhhhhhhhhhhhhhhhhhhhhhhh!!!!'

Too late! The Vet will now be withdrawing the needle with relish and looking towards you with a grin which not only contains satisfaction but also relief – the prospect of maybe going on holiday this year, and even being able to address the patches in the bodywork of the shooting brake.

'Good . . . thank you for being so understanding,' he will say. 'I'm glad you agreed so readily. Perhaps you could just give me a couple of blank cheques and I'll fill in the amount later?'

He will still be brandishing the hypodermic at you with a certain amount of threat, so you will meekly comply, your mind weakened, not only by the turn of events, but also Dodo's latest assault.

With that, he'll be gone, to be replaced several minutes later by your partner, who will saunter up to you, while you are still clutching your throbbing foot and nonchalantly say: 'Has he gone then?'

'Yes...' you will say. Then you will add, pathetically: 'Helen – just *how* much do you owe him on this 𝕽unning 𝕱arm 𝕬ccount thing...?'

'Oh *that*,' she will say. 'What on *earth* do you want to know about *that* for. No one ever pays *that* . . .'

HOW BARMY IS YOUR PARTNER?

Having now understood a few basic principles about how you got into this mess in the first place, what you are dealing with in terms of your arch enemy, the horse, and the realisation that you **must** fend for yourself, it is time to discuss your partner in a little more detail.

The first point to remember is that your partner *hates* riding horses and *hates* everything to do with them. That's why she spends so much time with them.

This is a very important lesson to learn because, unless you come to terms with the whole barmy state of affairs, you will never be able to understand why your partner expends so much energy, money, effort, time, trauma and tears over something which clearly brings her no pleasure at all, and which seems to require round-the-clock commitment in order to be rewarded by so few days in the year when she is actually in the saddle.

The calendar for the horse year, as you will very rapidly come to understand, shapes up something like this:

January –   No riding, danger of ice and snow

February –   Likewise

March –   Spring may be on the way, but the ground is still too hard

April –   Ah, yes. Maybe the odd day's ride is possible but ground still seems a little too hard perhaps?

May –   Yes. Riding possible, as long as the horse is not lame – which unfortunately he seems to be

June –   No riding, I am afraid. The horse has recovered from lameness, but now the heat of the summer is beginning to take its toll, and it is simply too hard in the heat of the day

July –   Same thing to report again, I am afraid – and now there is the added problem of flies which seem to stick to every inch of the horse's head like glue

August –   The same as July, but worse. (Hotter and more humid, you see)

September –   Still some flies, but generally riding may be possible – but, hang on a minute, the horse is looking lame again

October –   Days have started to get a tad too short. If riding is possible, then it's only a few hours at the weekend – but check his withers first

November –   Hardly any daylight now, and what's more the ground's too hard again

December –   First snows of winter. Definitely no riding.

Now, added to that is the fact that on the very few days in the calendar when they actually get to ride the beast you very rapidly begin to realise that the actual business of going out on it gives your partner no pleasure at all. In fact it gives her something between abject horror, loathing, fear, dread and misery.

The build up to the event goes something like this:

After the initial pre-dawn ritual of muckfrollicking you will be revived from your slumbers by the bald statement:

'I think I'll take Dodo out for a ride.'

This is followed by a sudden solemn and significant silence which seems to pervade the very air in which your breath, followed by a period of anxious pacing up and down. The decision has been made. There is no going back now, but your partner has now realised that she has let herself in for something which is truly *dreadful*.

So you get a littany of ever increasing anxt as in: 'I hope the ground's all right . . . then there's the flies . . . God they're bad today . . . almost closed up both of his eyes . . . you know, I think he looked a little lame when I was with him earlier on . . . no, *can't* be . . . on the other hand I suppose he *could* be . . . and the flies won't help . . . and the ground . . . what if the ground's too hard . . . that won't do his lameness any good . . . what do you think? . . . do you think I should go out? . . . WELL **DO YOU???!!!!'**

Now, at this point be very careful indeed. *Your* role is to be encouraging. If you were to speak your mind, and give an honest answer to the question, you would say something like: 'No for God's sake, I can't stand this any longer . . . I don't think you should go out riding if this is how it is every time you go out . . . why don't you have the bloody thing melted down for glue and let's go to Majorca for the weekend!'

But anyone who's been in the horse world for five minutes knows that's not the answer.

If you were foolish enough to say such a thing you would immediately realise the error of your ways as in the icy stare, the sudden sullen brooding, smouldering silence and then the ' . . . that's so **TYPICAL** of you . . . trying to ruin **ALL** my pleasures . . . well it won't work this time . . . I'm going riding . . . and I'll probably not come back!'

So it follows that a careful answer will be something along the lines of: 'Yes, of course you must go riding . . . it's such a lovely day, and I'm sure the flies won't be that bad . . .'

This will, in its initial instance create another period of apparent indecision and anxt much along the lines of before, but eventually the moment will arrive and your partner will go, laden down with all the tack [we'll come on to what this means later] that has been all over the floor of every room in the house ever since the last time she actually achieved lift off, about six weeks before.

You will say something like: ' Have a really nice time.'

To which she will reply: 'I'm not so *sure* about that.'

Now, what you should also understand at this point is that lift off can still be aborted. So don't kid yourself that you are in for a peaceful couple of hours reading the paper. Before the actual moment of getting in the saddle and tally-ho-ing into the far blue yonder, there is a period of upwards to an hour when all the preparation rituals take place [we'll come on to *those* later on, too] and that is ample time for your partner to notice that after all the beast *is* lame – so no riding today.

In such an event, you will receive the full force of disappointment, that *coitus interruptus* of unfulfilled endeavour meted upon your head.

Usually this takes the form of a slamming of the door, tack thrown all over the floor and to your polite enquiry: 'You're back early dear???', you will get a mumbled reply heavily laden with the undertone of 'Don't push your luck buster', which will inform you that the cherished mount is unrideable today.

Then, as you prepare a comforting cup of coffee, you will be ignored, while your partner finds a sudden and indefatigable urge to inform all and sundry in the horsey fraternity of the tragic loss.

When she emerges, tired and emotional, some two hours later, she will require a comforting arm and understanding, and then you will be informed ominously: 'If he goes on like this, I'm going to have to get the Vet in to have a look at him.'

If, on the other hand, the mission achieves a successful lift off [and you will know this from the non-appearance of your partner after about an hour] then it would be only natural for you to assume that not only are you in for a couple of peaceful hours to yourself, but also that, on return, your partner will be fulfilled, refreshed, a much happier person than when she left, with all those anxious feelings of anxiety purged from her body.

Er...not so, I'm afraid.

Return, on this occasion, has the same familiar ring to it as aborted lift-off had done – except that it happens about two hours later.

The door is slammed just as in the other scenario. The tack reaches the floor just as quickly, and your partner's demeanour is just the same.

This time, you will say something like: 'Had a good ride dear???'

That same laden undertone is present in the voice as the reply comes back: 'NO, I've had a **DREADFUL** time. First he carted me down the field, then he bucked and reared at a tractor . . . I mean to say, a bloody tractor . . . how many tractors are there in this world for God's sake . . . . and he has to be the only horse in the whole of Christendom who's bloody well scared of them . . . and then he rammed me into a tree . . . just look at this bruise . . . JUST LOOK!!! . . . that's already starting to go black . . . then he dumped me on the road . . . how on earth I haven't received any serious injuries I'll never know...and then to cap it all . . . I think the bastard's gone lame . . . so I don't know when I'm going to be able to ride him . . . I bet it's another six weeks . . . and I'm going to have to have the Vet in . . .'

Now – a word of warning: whatever you do, **DON'T** at this point either say something stupid like: 'Doesn't sound as though it's gone too well then?' or something sarcastic like: 'It's all part of life's rich tapestry dear, in the wonderful world of horses . . .'

The first remark is liable to lead to instant divorce on the grounds that you are a terminal imbecile, while the latter is likely to lead to an even more instant ending of your relationship, via the carving knife.

What you must do is **stay calm,** nod benignly, mutter the occasional 'oh dear', and **be practical,** like offering to pay for the Vet when he comes. You are going to end up paying for him anyway, but this way, it makes you look **helpful** and **encouraging** [and as we have already seen at least you won't have to clear up decades of 𝕽𝖚𝖓𝖓𝖎𝖓𝖌 𝕱𝖆𝖗𝖒 𝕬𝖈𝖈𝖔𝖚𝖓𝖙 𝕴𝖓𝖙𝖊𝖗𝖊𝖘𝖙 as well] and then you might even get to spend a few sainted hours [after the statutory phone calls have been laid in to all the other members of the horsey fraternity that is – you're never going to escape those, I'm afraid] doing a few non-horsey things, like breathing and eating.

If you follow this advice, then you will have learned yet another lesson in survival.

Now: at this point you might feel in a very self-congratulatory sort of mood, but I am afraid that you have no time for that. Things are moving all the time in the wonderful world of horses, and they move very quickly as well, so no sooner have you conquered this particular problem than another one looms up over the horizon.

Just as you thought you had attained some measure of achievement, your hopes will be dashed. As the ritual end-of-the-ride calls are made, inevitably someone somewhere in the long anecdotal calls will remind your partner that the very next day there is another **event**. And this time, instead of a casual ride in the country, this will be something involving jumping over obstacles which are of a size which would dwarf the Empire State Building, judging from your partner's reaction.

The moment the telephone goes down, you realise you are in for it all over again.

First of all, there is the introductory statement: 'Claire tells me that there's an open jumping competition at the Sterling-Smythes tomorrow. You don't mind if I go, do you?'

Remember always that this statement, although it appears to give you the option, in fact it give you no option at all. What it is in fact actually saying is: ' I *AM* going but it makes me feel a great deal better if you agree with that fact. Then I can go without any pangs of conscience – not that I was going to have any anyway . . .'

So, first of all **NEVER** remind her that she suggested that her prize mount was going lame, not all that many minutes ago. That would be fatally unhelpful, and probably carry with it some sort of disparaging remark like: 'Oh, since when have you been a Vet?'

What you have to say is something along the lines of: 'No, I don't mind at all. You go and have a *really good time.* I can easily re-arrange the flights to Barbados, or better still, give the tickets to some bloke down the pub. After all, *anybody* can go to Barbados *any* time.'

You will then be bombarded with ever more emphatic rejoinders of: 'Now, you really are **sure** aren't you? You don't *really* mind? **SURE????**'

To which you must be ever more emphatic in your denials, even if you may be inwardly spitting blood.

Then, the emphasis will subtly change. In the middle of all these questions and denials, your partner will suddenly drop in: ' Mind you, I must need my head looking at even thinking of going . . . have you seen the SIZE of the jumps on that course . . . ?'

Here we go again. Here beginneth the next bout of anxt and I'm afraid all you are going to have to do is to survive it.

From here on it will be: 'They're flippin' enormous . . . far bigger than anything I've ever attempted before . . . my God, they're over 2ft 6in . . . TWO FOOT SIX . . . do you know how **BIG** that is . . . **THAT'S BIG!!!** . . . I must be mad . . . **MAD!!!!** . . . he'll *never* clear TWO FOOT SIX . . . I'll need a vallium . . . Val has vallium before she goes over that course . . . now I know why . . . MY GOD . . . I'VE RUN OUT . . . and there's NO WAY I'm going over that course without SOMETHING to calm my nerves . . . he'll pick up on it STRAIGHT AWAY of I'm at all nervous . . . then he'll go bananas . . . I know it . . . do you think Brandy will help . . . do you think I should take a hip flask or something . . . by the way my will is in the top draw of the filing cabinet . . . '

This will go on for the next four hours or so, as you try to get through the rest of the day with as much of your own sanity intact as possible, before the magic hour of 8pm arrives and your partner will then announce that she is going to bed as it is **absolutely vital** that she gets to bed early as it will be a 4am start the next day.

DON'T whatever you do question why there has to be such an early start, when she isn't going to be going round the course until 3.30 pm the following day. If you do, you will then have a list of all the tedious and niggling things that have to be done before lift off – rounding off with the sting in the tail:' . . . and you aren't much help . . .' which indicates that your perfectly innocent question has in fact contributed to the running tally of negatives you have been building up ever since you first entered this relationship.

Which will then bring us on to the next fatal stumbling block you are bound to encounter – because in the list of things that must be done before the following day's big event, there will inevitably be: ' . . . and I've got to do my tack . . .'

NOW: before you got yourself involved in the horsey world, you probably thought that the term "Tack" related to a type of short nail that is used in furniture making.

Not so. You only have to be around the horsey world for a short while to realise that the term relates also to a weird and wonderful array of objects which look like instruments of torture. And are.

I won't dwell here on the complexities of the whole inventory of these items, because I am well aware that I don't know it – and there's probably only a few privileged souls in the entire universe who are entrusted with this knowledge. But it is important that you get a solid grounding in what tack is all about so that you can survive its dark excesses.

One of the most important elements of Tack is the Bit. This is the stick like object they put in the horse's mouth to keep him in order as they are riding. It resembles the sort of thing they used to put in a patient's mouth in those days before anaesthetic, when they were about to take his leg off.

Now: you might think that it was as simple as that – a sort of something, shaped like a stick, that they stick in the horse's mouth.

WRONG AGAIN, I am afraid.

What *you* might refer to as a "Bit", to *them* has a whole vocabulary of strange sounding names – almost like those meaningless terms which they use on obscure sports programmes or to denote types of dives in diving competitions, or, more often the types of manoeuvres they carry out in ice skating. Terms like "Double Axle", "Triple Salko", "Pike with Tuck", "Triple Toe Loop", "Half Nelson", "Forearm Smash" and "Right Upper Cut" and so on and so forth.

You might not think this any more important than a mere academic interest. Rather like watching the skating, or whatever it is you watch. After all, it's rather nice to know that whoever you are watching has just put in a rather tasty Triple Axle followed by a Double Salko combination, but it hardly makes any difference to your life.

When it comes to Bits, however, the first thing that you have to understand is that whatever your partner is using on her horse, it is definitely the wrong one. And as a result there is a constant problem.

This is usually manifested by what might seem to be at first a casual remark such as:

'You know, I'm sure he's not happy in that Twin Snaffle.'

Don't worry what on earth this term means – just remember that anything with this sort of name is a 'Bit', so don't for goodness sake make the crass mistake of saying something stupid like: ' . . . a Twin *what???*'

Again, just nod benignly as though you know what your partner is talking about and then let her go on, because by now she will have gone into speculating mode, as evidenced by the rather gormless stare into space as she considers the problem. You will then inevitably be confronted with a set of terms which mean absolutely nothing to you, but you **must** go along with it. It will go something like this:

' I've tried him in a Pelham, and that didn't work out, then it was the Fat Lady and golly what a disaster that was . . . Joan thinks I should try him in a Jointed Ring Snaffle . . . but I'm not convinced . . . I could put him in a Kimberwick, or perhaps a Scamperdale . . . or a Ward Union Club . . . but Sam the other day was saying that the best solution might have to be a Gag . . . what do you think?'

Yes, you heard right. Your partner is asking your opinion on something you have not the slightest inkling of knowledge about. But unfortunately you're right on the spot because, ominously, she's come out of speculating mode and is now looking straight at you with a steely look of interrogation.

The silence at this point is often deafening.

NOW: whatever you do, you *must* give an opinion, but *for Goodness sake DON'T* give the opinion regarding the **Gag** which is uppermost in your mind at that moment, nor *WHATEVER YOU DO, NEVER* invent a smartarse type of bit of your own such as: 'Why don't you put him in French Revolution Guillotine?' Such a course of action is *EXTREMELY ILL ADVISED.*

The best thing to do is to look as though you are really considering the question and then refer the matter to someone who you think your partner regards as having a half decent opinion such as: ' Have your thought of asking Robin?'

You will either get something like [at best] 'That's a thought . . . thanks.' Or [at sort of OK]: 'I've already asked him, but he couldn't come up with an idea either.'

If you get the latter, don't despair because at the very least you've proved to be helpful rather than useless or disparaging, and what's more, you've elevated your opinion, in this instance at least, to the level of Robin, which means that you cannot be counted as anything worse than him, and, as he's the acknowledged bloke with a half decent opinion, you can't come in for any further criticism. So, you've survived again.

There are plenty of other bits, of course, and I am sorry to have to report that Bits are only one form of tack. You will have to do your best at surviving the major crises which each of them, in their own turn, will bring into your life. Some of them will be familiar, and it is likely you will have heard of them in your previous non-horsey days – like the 'Bridle', for example.

Many more, however, will be so unfamiliar that it is hardly likely you will have heard of them, and quite frankly you will probably never ever get to learn what they are for – like the 'Crupper' [yes, I said C.R.*U*.P.P.E.R. – what you thought I said is, well, something else], the 'Browband', the 'Martingale' and the 'Throatlash' – **DON'T** be tempted into speculation on that last one by the way.

The one thing to bear in mind always about these bits and pieces is that they are ALL essential to the whole business of riding, and on EVERY OCCASION, one at least will go missing from the general piles of tack which seem to grow by organic processes out of your carpet.

Like general infestation you might even find odd bits where you hardly expect them to turn up, like behind books in your bookcase, in the video cabinet or under the occasional floor board.

In each case, when this happens, you can rest assured that it was once a most cherished item, it went missing at just the wrong time, and therefore had to be replaced with three identical pieces of tack, which were bought at what to you might seem enormous expense but REALLY WERE snapped up at a snip price because they came at the end of a tack auction, and which unfortunately all now seem to be lost themselves, so finding the damn thing has come in rather useful – or it would have done had she not had to go to the horse shop to buy six more to replace the three replacements which themselves eventually went missing.

In such an event, just glow with reflected pride that you had some hand in bringing this happy and supportive chain of events to pass.

The next item which is on the agenda while we have this general overview of tack is

THE SADDLE

Now: you've probably heard of this one, so it is pointless discussing the various important aspects of it, except to say that it is vital you understand the next general guiding principle of the horse world:

> Your partner's saddle will always be the wrong one for the horse.

This is an important element in horsecraft, because this general guideline gleefully guarantees the horsey person with two basic requirements –

1. It ensures that they will never enjoy any ride they go on, and

2. It ensures that they are always spending pots of money they haven't got, trying to replace the saddle they have with one which is equally unacceptable.

Just how the saddle is unacceptable is not for the likes of you, by the way. Just accept it as a stated fact. Occasionally you will be given a general indication. You will hear that it's either too big, or too small, or doesn't fit the horse in a vital area – so it can be both too big and too small at the same time – or else it's made from the wrong material. But you will never get to know exactly.

But as I say, just accept this fact for what it is, and **DON'T SAY ANYTHING** as the piles of saddles grow beside the organic clusters of growing tack, and **CERTAINLY** curb your tongue if you happen to trip over the odd one sitting uncomfortably in the middle of the room. You will only be chided for damaging the saddle.

You may be forgiven at this point if you think that awareness of tack and generally having a vague idea of what it does is about as far as you need to know about it.

Unfortunately, again you are wrong.

This is because sooner or later [and believe me, it will *undoubtedly* be sooner], you will find yourself –

INTERACTING WITH TACK

There's no escape from this, I am afraid. It comes upon you in the most unsuspecting sort of way.

A typical scenario will be on a Sunday morning [a no-riding-activity – Sunday that is]. As you sit there contemplating the headlines and deliciously devouring the possibilities of an in depth analysis of some vital inter-personal complexity lurking deeply within the body of a whole slab of copy carrying the headline: 'BONKING BOB CRACKED HIS CONKERS ON CORKING CAROL'S CLUTCH', you will hear a distant cry for help.

On enquiring you will find your partner wrestling with something which looks from the outset like a series of leather straps. As you approach, still in innocent abandon, these straps will start to take on a more familiar look about them.

It is only when you have passed the point of no return, and you are fully in view of your partner, and in earshot of the pleading ' can you give me a hand with this then?' will you realise that what she has in her hand is, well, a piece of tack.

This will then be handed to you with the nonchalant request that you release one strap impossibly tangled in an uncompromising looking piece of ironwork.

There is no point in trying to wriggle out of it. You are hooked as surely as any fish on the line. The only thing you can do is carry out the request, realising, as soon as you have taken the items into your hand, that your partner miraculously disappears.

You then have to face the inevitability of sorting the matter out. To do otherwise would bring with it the damning accusation that you are nothing more than a wimp, followed by the ominous promise that Adrian [*who* the *hell* is *ADRIAN* for *GOD'S SAKE!!!!*] will be asked to perform the task instead.

So you have no choice but to wrestle for the next half hour, losing nail after nail, and cutting your fingers to ribbons, before you finally realise that brute force simply won't work. All that is required is that you slip the lug of the ironwork deftly through the hole over there, bring the strap into the vertical position and the whole thing just falls apart in your hands. Simple eh?

Whatever kudos you feel you may have earned through this process may or may not reap its rewards with a muttered 'thanks' as though it was a test from which she didn't really believe you would emerge unscathed, and now, deep down, she's pretty peeved.

But of course once you have settled down to the BONKING LOVE RAT BOB again, you will inevitably face the request you have been dreading [if you are used to this sort of thing by now, that is] that you now

PUT THE WHOLE DAMN THING BACK TOGETHER AGAIN

Again, you can't escape. You were the one that caused it to fall into a thousand pieces in the first place. So you *must* know how it goes back together. After all, Adrian would.

And you can forget any further thoughts you might have harboured about discovering the ultimate fate of BONKING LOVE RAT WIFE STEALING SHAMED 'I WOULDN'T WALK ON THE SAME SIDE OF THE STREET AS HIM' BOB, because while you were tackling the second phase of your Sunday morning tack duties, your partner had decided to employ herself busily with cleaning her saddle, and of course she needed some newspaper, so the last you see of BONKING LOVE RAT WIFE STEALING 'I WOULDN'T WALK ON THE SAME SIDE OF THE STREET AS HIM', I WAS AN INEXPERIENCED VIRGIN MOTHER OF 19 WHEN I FIRST MET HIM, THE PERVE, BOB is as his soaking wet smiling sanctimonious image disappears into the first available garbage sack in the back yard.

Another regular tack scenario involves you in the presence of the horse itself.

This usually takes the form of a similar request to the one listed above, but this time while you are standing like a spare part beside the sainted beast wondering what on earth you are going to do with the rest of your life hereon.

As various lifestyles flash through your troubled mind – astronaut, deep sea diver, coal miner [no, sorry, not that one – they use horses sometimes don't they?] your reverie will be awakened by the plea: 'Can you do this up for me?'

'This' in this instance is the **GIRTH** – the strap that holds the whole horse/rider combination together – which is also a combination of strapwork and uncompromising iron.

It is never tight enough, even though, in this instance you may even have a fleeting feeling for the horse who seems to be having difficulty breathing.

If you make the inevitable stupid remark that it seems tight enough to you, you immediately begin to learn that old horsey is a cunning beast [you *don't* say!] and he apparently deliberately breaths out as soon as the girth is put around him, to make it impossible to join the damned thing up.

You may speculate at this point as to how a creature such as this could have perfected the art of holding its breath for the thirty minutes or so that it took your partner to put on all the saddlery, tack and other instruments of the torture chamber with which the horse has now been attired. You may also note on the way the he seems to be some two feet thinner in the vicinity of the girth than the rest of him.

But what do you know about it anyway? You are only there to serve and as there is nowhere for you to hide, all you can do is obey.

As you struggle with the strapwork which refuses to budge, and stub your fingers and thumbs on the metal protrusions of buckles and bows, try to calm yourself with the knowledge that you are being extremely helpful.

And that once you have completed your task, not only will you be left in peace for the next hour or so [lameness permitting of course] but the wretched beast might actually expire on the way.

Which now brings me to the next instruments of torture – and these are BIG ONES.

SHOES

Remember in those heady days of long ago, when you were a child, and wandered lonely and free in the country, if you were lucky you might happen upon a discarded horseshoe, rusting peacefully away at the side of the trackway.

Believing all that rubbish about horseshoes being lucky you carefully took the object back home where a benign parent, unable to ring Social Services for some helpful counselling advice, because Social Services didn't exist in those days, would console you by suggesting that you nailed the thing up above your bedroom door.   That way, it would give you luck.

Actually, there was some primitive truth in this old wives tale – if good fortune can be bestowed upon he who heeds all dire warnings – because what you should have understood from this talisman hoisted above your bedroom door was the fact that back in the mists of ancient time, blokes dressed up in loin cloths and woad issued their strange and significant edicts for the further health of the common man – but unfortunately like all legends which have corroded a little bit during the past few thousands years this message lost its original meaning and became bestowed with all this 'good luck' crap.   You see, what the ancient ones were actually trying to say was:

NEVER HAVE ANYTHING TO DO WITH HORSES

Still, there is little point in looking back over past mistakes.   Unfortunately it is far too late for you to make redress.

There is also little to be gained from me reminding you that these articles, far from being good luck charms are the root cause of you standing hour after hour in the open air, at great risk of serious injury, in the pouring rain.   And of course they are one of the main reasons why *you* don't seem to be able to go on holiday like everyone else, why *your* car seems to be getting a little on the old side, and why *you* and your partner seem to save going to the supermarket until the last half hour on a Saturday night when everything seems to be carrying those red or yellow discount labels – so that *your* trolley seems to be full of all those really useful everyday items like out of date stuffing.

It will also need no reminders from me that the one fact about horse shoes which should be understood from the beginning is that:

they hardly ever seem to stay on the horse.

Not a week goes by, it seems, without a distraut partner coming home early from projected lift off with that self same slam of the door, explosion of tack on the floor and the dull and sullen expression on her face as she makes for the telephone for the ritual calls.

Those who have not fully entered the wonderful world of horses or naive raw recruits might at this point offer something like: 'Don't tell me he's gone lame again?'

To say such a thing would be strongly ill advised. For a start it is not up to you to offer a diagnosis. After all, when did *you* become a Vet, so what do *you* know?

You must wait to be informed because, more likely than lameness is: 'The bastard's cast a shoe!!!'

When you hear this, **DON'T** whatever you do sigh in delighted relief. True this calamity will not mean calling in the Vet – there will be no mention of the 𝕽unning 𝕱arm 𝕬ccount this time – but if you think that this mere fact will remove the necessary expense, then I'm afraid you are tragically mistaken.

Without question, the first call of the ritual round on the telephone will be to:

THE FARRIER

The Farrier is what you probably have called a Blacksmith in days gone by. Don't for goodness sake ever ask what the difference is. There is enough trouble brewing as it is.

Now: the Farrier won't be in. He never is. So you will just have to wait for ten minutes while your partner listens to the answerphone message and then all the jingly little tunes which follow it, indicating the stack of messages which have built up from similarly distraut horsey people desperate for the Farrier that morning, before it becomes her turn to gush with her tale of woe on the receiving tape the other end.

It would, to say the least, be churlish of you, in the middle of all this anguish and pain, to start counting the cost of a ten minute wait at prime time on the telephone. At any rate, it is only a fraction of the cost of what is to come. Almost infinitesimal in fact.

Anyway, you won't get much chance to voice your opinion. As soon as the phone has gone down on the Farrier, it will be picked up again to tell Tess, Jenny, Sally, Bunty and all points of the compass what has occurred.

All you can do from here on is wait.

While we are waiting [you will see what for later on] it is a good time to review some

FACTS ABOUT FARRIERS

We have already discussed one – that they are never in when your distraut partner desperately needs them.

Which leads me to another very important fact: that Farriers have so much work coming out of their ears, that they don't know what to do with it. You probably gathered that from the fact that it takes ten minutes wait on the answer phone before your partner can blubber her tragedy to add to the rest.

It follows that anyone with more work than they know what to do with can well afford to be extremely selective. Which means that any Farrier worth his salt will not suffer fools gladly. Neither will he work on behalf of anyone who tries to boss him around, nor, incidentally, anyone with a large nose.

Yes, he can be *that* selective – even down to the point of downright rudeness such as: 'Sorry Bunty, your nose is just *too big,* I wouldn't shoe your nag even for a million until you agree to undergo plastic surgery. And, by the way, has anyone told you your bum's too big as well?'

It does not take a genius to understand from a very early point in dealing with the Farrier therefore, that, not only must you make sure that your facial furniture is up to acceptable levels, but you must also be **Extremely Respectful.**

Any deviation from abjectivity will be severely punished, such as: ' You can stuff it from now on. You'll just have to get someone else . . . and by the way when I said you had a big bum, what I really meant was that it is so big that I've only just realised that total eclipses of the sun don't really occur every time I shoe your horse . . . which I won't do from now on.'

All of which means that your partner and everyone else in the horsey world for that matter will always treat the Farrier with **utmost respect.**

Although they won't actually call him 'Sir' [such terminology is only reserved for the Gentry types, of which more anon] they will nevertheless call him by his name, be it Tony, Clive, Steve, Alan or whatever monica he celebrates under in a way which has the same *respectful* inflection.

So when he says something like: " I think he [the horse that is]needs special heavy duty therapeutic [and therefore *incredibly expensive*] shoes this time . . . "

She:

(a) won't argue

and

(b) will say something like: "Yes, of course. What*ever* you say . . . *Tony*."

And if he says something which would earn you an instant divorce petition, such as: 'Aren't you *ever* going to get those dreadful buck teeth of yours sorted out. You're beginning to look like a donkey, fat arse . . .'

She will merely titter uncontrollably and say something like: 'Oh *Tony*, you *do* jest . . .' in much the same way that one of the courtiers at the court of Henry VIII must have reacted when the Merry Monarch told him that unless he brushed up his image and agreed to send his wife to the Royal Bedchamber for a bit of rumpy pumpy for the next few weeks, he would have his head chopped off.

Which brings me to one rather curious fact about the Farrier which I must admit often used to puzzle me.

Given this omnipotence in a world largely populated by women, and given also both opportunity and no lack of red corpuscles coursing their way through his rippling biceps [and in other parts of his bronzed physique, if you get my drift], I have yet to come across a Farrier who turns this situation into a sexual advantage.

This is made all the more curious by the fact that every genuinely horsey man I have ever met in the horse world seemed to have got involved for just that reason [of which more later].

For some years, I was totally bemused by this – at first thinking that perhaps there was some sort of elaborate conspiracy, then moving on to thinking that perhaps the majority of women in the wonderful world of horses were simply not fanciable and then, bizarrely for about a minute or so, wondering whether the horsey world was just one humungus gay dating agency.

But then it struck me, like a bolt out of the blue on the road to Damascus [or something like that] –

THE FARRIER IS THE MOST PERFECT HORSE HATER THAT EXISTS ON EARTH

He is to be both admired and envied by the rest of us. He it is, who, from an extremely early age was able to 'come out' with his true feelings about horses, and then carried it through with

training and dedication to the point where he gets not only maximum satisfaction but also enormous sums of money exacting the most excruciating torment on his more than willing victims.

In short, he is everything that you or I would wish to be, but can't because *we* trained to be brain surgeons, merchant bankers etc etc.

When you realise this all important fact, it is easy to see how everything in the Farrier's behaviour falls neatly into place.

For a start he really is there when your partner telephones in desperation. He is sitting at home, by the answerphone, knocking back the odd glass of Vintage Bollinger 1863, while listening to the ever mounting tales of woe, and laughing gleefully to himself as he dusts his old master paintings, or polishes the Roller packed prettily on the pink Italian marble patio outside.

Then, as he relaxes by the side of the pool in the languid atmosphere with the aid of a heady post prandial pina colada, while he nudges the pages of a travel brochure advertising all inclusive safaris along the Amazon, he may review the tape again, chuckling inwardly to himself as he muses: "That's the third time this month for Nellie the Elephant, it will have to be the special heavy duty therapeutic [and therefore *incredibly expensive*] ones this time."

At the appropriate hour, usually long into the night, when you and your partner have been in bed for hours, he will then chose to set in motion his master plan.

The first you will know of this course of events will be the urgent summons of the telephone in the midst of your slumbers.

You will answer and be strangely concerned to hear a man's voice on the other end of the line:

[The Voice] 'Mr Squib?'

[You – trying to sound very macho, so therefore putting on a ridiculously deeper version of your voice than normal] 'Ye-e-e-e-ssss'

[The Voice] 'It's Tony, Mr Squib. Tony the Farrier. I'm returning your wife's call'

At this point, the initial relief that it's not Adrian [yes, *him* again!!] will be followed almost immediately by a stabbing depression as you pass the phone over to your partner, who, on realising that this is the FARRIER will immediately emerge from the protecting veil of the bedclothes and a *wonderful* dream all about ponies, to sit upright in an 'At Attention' sort of posture.

The conversation will then go something like this:

[Your Partner] 'Hello *Tony* [yes . . . you've recognised it, in that supine voice as in 'Sir']. How good of you to phone back.'

You're probably casting an eye towards the clock by now, and registering that it is indicating 2.30am, leading you to have perhaps somewhat different thoughts to your partner, but *DON'T* express them.

[Tony] 'Sorry I've not come back to you before now, but as you can imagine, I'm desperately busy at the moment.'

[Your Partner] 'Yes. Of course. You must be rushed off your feet. How *terrible*. You need a holiday.'

[Tony: having difficulty suppressing his glee] 'Yes. That's what I'm telephoning now for, I'm afraid. You see, I'm fully booked until the end of the week, then I'm catching a short holiday, so I'm afraid I won't be able to come over until after I get back.'

[Your Partner – subsiding into good old British 'stiff-upper-lip' mode in a desperate and fruitless attempt to conceal her abject despair] 'Oh . . . that's a shame . . . but I suppose it can't be helped. How long are you going for?'

[Tony] 'Only a short break this time . . . just the six weeks.'

[Your Partner] 'Oh . . . that's good.   Not as long as the other two breaks this year then . . . going somewhere nice?'

[Tony] 'Nothing special.   Can't afford too much . . . so we decided to give the Dominican Republic a try this time . . . one of those all inclusive jobs, you know.'

[Your Partner] 'Oh . . . sounds nice.   Can't say that I've ever thought of the Dominican Republic . . . with the horse and the expense and the commitment and all, we only managed a few hours in a tent at Weston Super Mare this year – before the Boy Scouts started their camp. Still, I hope you have a **great time** *Tony* – if anyone deserves it, *you* do.'

[Tony: now so beside himself with mirth he can hardly speak] ' So sorry about this . . . still I've put you down as **first on the list** for when I get back.'

[Your Partner: now so beside herself with effulgent gratitude *she* can hardly speak either] 'Oh . . . do you mean it . . . oh thanks *so much, Tony*.'

At that she will put down the telephone, and burst into tears – tears of desperation, tears of gratitude, tears of, well, just tears.

You will say something like: ' He can't come tomorrow then?'

If you do, then you will get one of those 'don't push it buster' looks which means that you are beginning to tread dangerous territory again.   In such an event, **YOU SHOULD NOT UNDER ANY CIRCUMSTANCES SAY THE FOLLOWING:**

'Why don't you try another Farrier.'

To say such a thing is so indescribably stupid as to be laughable.

In the first instance, you must KNOW that Tony [sorry] *Tony* is without question the ONLY FARRIER IN THE WORLD who understands Dodo's problem hooves and apart from that HE'S THE BEST THERE IS.   What you are saying is TANTAMOUNT TO UNDERMINING THE WHOLE FABRIC OF THE HORSEY HIERARCHY.

As far as your partner is concerned *Tony* is her master, and she is his serf.   She could no more transfer to another Farrier than could a medieval bondsman switch his allegiance from one liege lord to another.

How Barmy Is Your Partner?

And anyway, six weeks' inactivity is not such a long time to wait, after all. And Dodo *was* looking a bit lame this morning. So it's all probably for the best.

Meanwhile, somewhere up a long and winding driveway, beyond the gatehouse and the servants' quarters, across the opulent expanses of the panelled drawing room, *Tony* is savouring the delicate flavour of the Chateau Yqueme 1776 which was delivered that very morning, and breathing heavily to himself with satisfaction that phase one of his master plan has been completed successfully.

He now has a list of two hundred distraut women, *all* of whom are so dreadfully grateful that he won't be able to come to see them for six weeks, but gushing with emotion that each and every one of them is going to be first on his list when he gets back.

Just think for a moment what an enviable situation he is now in. While *you* spend the next six weeks dealing with the mounting tensions and withdrawal symptoms caused by this enforced inactivity, *he* will be soaking up the sunshine with gay abandon as he plots the second phase of his masterplan. And the second phase is without doubt the most satisfying.

It begins some days after the allotted time when he had promised to come. As you watch your partner gradually waste away in front of your eyes and the anxiety mount on her pallid brow, you cannot but feel that pang of admiration for this man who can bring about such a complete and utter demolition of the world you have found yourself in.

Then, comes the telephone call. Like the sounding of the last trumpet on the day of judgement.

Using what fingers she has left after all the nail biting and white knuckle exercises, your partner will grab the receiver and in much the same way as someone desperate for a fix.

The reward will be the promise that he's on his way **and will be at the field in half an hour.**

Such an announcement will spur your partner into a flurry of activity. Day to day clothing will be immediately dispensed with. Jods pulled over that rather over large posterior and boots smelling like the hind quarters of a donkey donned with ardent expectation.

It will be pointless to remind her at this point that your brother is getting married in 20 minutes or so, or some other trivial diversion.

Without any further ado, she will have disappeared long before you will be able to mouth any further words along the line of: " . . . but I'm supposed to be his Best Man . . ."

But this is where the Farrier plays his second masterstroke.

He won't turn up for another four hours.

This is especially the case if it is in the middle of winter, or is pouring down with rain. Somewhat less if it is a nice sunny day and he feels that your partner might actually be *enjoying* the fresh air.

At the moment he telephoned, he was probably emerging from the sauna before having attention from his personal masseuse while reviewing his holdings in conglomerates with his stockbroker on his personal video link. Then it was a round of golf on the links he had built on the set-aside acres out at the back of the stately home, before reviewing the time, and changing from his tweeds into the cheque lumberjack style shirt and jeans which seems to be the Farrier's uniform, putting away the Roller into its purpose built garage, and setting off in the ten year old transit which has been carefully transformed into a torture chamber on wheels.

When he arrives at the field where your partner has now virtually frozen to death and is barely indistinguishable from the trees standing in the hedgerows, he will offer no apology. Indeed, it will be your partner who will offer thanks for him making it at all.

At this point, phase two will be complete and phase three will begin. Now, he can take his continuing revenge upon horses.

How many of us would wish to be in his position? Our partners, supine and passive standing like a spare part on the end of a lead rein, not a word coming from their lips, unless they are spoken to.

The horse, standing there, shivering both from the cold and in abject terror at what is about to happen.

And the Farrier, merrily stoking up his furnace to white heat intensity, as he grapples with iron and steel to forge them into the most devastating instruments of pain and pleasure.

Then the nail, banged in with abandon with the lump hammer which will inevitably be brought to bear upon the animal if ever it seeks to complain – and often when it doesn't appear to be complaining that much.

Which all adds up to a pretty good afternoon for the Farrier particularly so when you consider that once all this innate latent bloodlust has been well and truly satisfied, and he wipes the beads of sweat from his brow which your partner may naively believe were caused by the intensity of his efforts, but which were actually caused by the climactic satisfaction of the afternoon's events, the inevitable question will be posed:

'How much do I owe you.'

to which he will stare blankly into her face, no doubt mentally measuring the dimensions of her nasal passages as he considers his verdict, and without further expression will say:
"Five hundred pounds."

So I ask you again: how many of us would wish to be in this exalted position? Able to exorcise all the ghosts of our lives in one tumultuous afternoon, and THEN to be able to charge for it.

It will be plainly seen, therefore, why there is no sexual motivation here. Bonking the customers has no place. The Farrier poses no threat to your relationship whatsoever. He's too busy planning his next pain and pleasure humiliation session – which will come, for you and your partner in about three or four weeks – holidays permitting that is.

Not that you could ever discuss the matter with the Farrier anyway. By the time you appear on the scene, he's long gone back to the canapés and caviar, leaving you to look longingly at the stub of the joint account cheque book which has just been dutifully written, before going back home to stare aimlessly at whatever featureless wall you can find.

EVENTS

On the few days in the year when your partner is able to ride, in consequence of the weather conditions, lack of shoes, lameness etc etc etc, you will find that in addition to not enjoying just going out for a non-pleasurable ride, she will not enjoy taking part in a more formal event – but she will not enjoy this to the point of hysterical terror.

Such a feeling is obviously very highly prized in the horsey world, because when you turn up to the event, you will find that there are hundreds of people taking part who are also in the same state of abject terror – all of whom will be saying the same: 'I must need my head looking at taking part in this . . .' sort of phrase. With this, of course, you can wholeheartedly agree, but NEVER SAY SO. Keep it to yourself.

Events are wide and varied, and, believe me, you will NEVER get to know what they are. Whatever you do, DON'T ASK for explanation because, as in the case with other dumb requests for information, you will be confronted by the same look of shock and shame coupled with the inquisitorial: 'You mean you DON'T KNOW???!!!' uttered in the same tone the Spanish Inquisition must have used to confront their victims.

The reason for this is that, just as the Spanish Inquisition could never be exactly *certain* whether the person they were torturing – Galileo for example – might have been harbouring a much better idea of the truth than their religious incantations and general mumbo-jumbo could actually come up with, then to ask a horsey person *what* a specific event *is*, means that they have to prove to you that they *know* what it is – and of course they don't have any more clue of it than *you* do.

You can prove this to yourself, if you are so minded, of course – though I'd strongly advise against it, because whatever satisfaction you might glean from this ploy, will be more than punished by sulks, sullen solemnity, reminders that you are 'piss useless when it comes to horses' and downright threats later on – but it's your choice I suppose.

All you have to do is simply stand your ground and when you receive the inevitable: 'You mean you DON'T KNOW???!!!', say something like: 'No . . . I'm afraid I don't [while no doubt thinking: 'What the bloody hell do you think I asked for in the first place, dumbo . . .'].

There will then be a moment's silence, followed by a spluttering: '. . . well . . . it's a kind of a . . . well, you know . . . it's a . . . well . . . sort of . . . event sort of thing . . .'

This will be followed by a dismissive gesture, and then a disparaging insult such as: 'But if you're not prepared to find out for yourself, then it just shows how little you care about me, doesn't it? I knew I should have married someone who was REALLY INTO HORSES . . .' [Yes . . . it's Adrian time again!!!].

Don't say I didn't warn you if this happens. If on the other hand your genuinely want to know what all these events are about, then perhaps the following might be helpful.

As a general rule, events happen far away, down impossible lanes, in places which need the combined cartographic knowledge of John Speed and the Ordnance Survey to find.

They are never advertised, as far as you can see, but nevertheless everyone who is in the horsey world 'knows' about them, so that when you turn up, everyone is there – and unlike you, who have been struggling for hours down the impossible lanes getting even more irate as each dead end and blind bend looms in front of you – *they* all seem to have been there for ever.

You may have realised by now, by the way, that your presence is almost always **mandatory** at events. You are required not only to provide transportation services, but also map reading skills. When you get there, you are needed as caterer and tack untangler, girth tightener, and general moral support.

You will, for example, be told on numerous occasions by your partner that she is 'mad to be here', to which you *must* reason with her and tell her that she will be OK and that nothing will happen. **Never** agree with her analysis.

You must also be there to assure her that the private health policy is in your top pocket and that you have already [with your map reading skills] worked out the quickest route to the nearest private hospital.

When she returns from taking part in the event, you will be there to be encouraging, listen to the second by second commentary of whatever has taken place, shout 'good boy' to the horse, to whom you will give encouraging pats on the side of his neck as each time you are informed how 'brilliantly' he did – 'he *really went well*' before you get into the next round of tack untangling, and then put a comforting arm around your partner's shoulders as she finds out that she has been eliminated from the event because she didn't do something she should have done [don't bother to enquire *what,* if you value your life].

At this you will be required to find the box of tissues, and then turn caterer again, either providing a damn refreshing cup of tea, or, in the case of a major elimination [you will know this because it will be accompanied by half an hour of head in hands and copious and ever more desperate cries of '**How** could I have been **SO STUPID!!!**] a gin and tonic [triple].

After several of these have been downed, it will be back to the lanes again for another bout of orienteering across the highways and bye-ways of Britain before you eventually find yourself, late into the night, arriving back at base.

This is a typical diary of an *event.* The big mystery is: what actually *takes place* in that space of time from when your partner leaves you to your own devices and when she returns.

This, of course, depends on *what* the event is, and perhaps it will be helpful if I could provide some pointers – though I'm not over confident that I can be too successful here because I've never actually found out.

From what I can gather, events are roughly divided into those which involve your partner dicing with death over jumps, be they in a parade ring – that's something called '*Showjumping*' – or far off in the distance – that's something called '*Cross Country*' – and those in which she dresses up like a dog's dinner and performs all sorts of strange manoeuvres in front of someone who you never see, because they are always sitting in a parked car. These sort of antics, I believe, are called '*Dressage*'.

Obviously, horsey people combine these two basis types of activity together to form other events – all of which have the sort of names that mean everything to horsey people [at least that's what they make out] and *nothing* to you. Here are a few just to conjure with for the time being:

Three Day Event. What actually happens here is not entirely clear, but it involves *Dressage* and *Jumping* in some sort of way and what's more, you know that you're at a *Three Day Event*, because you are there for **three days**.

One Day Event. This differs from the above, because it happens over **one day**. But everything that happens at a *Three Day Event* seems to happen at a *One Day Event*, or so I'm told. You may wonder why there is a need for stringing out over three days, everything that seems to be contained quite adequately over one day, but it's a waste of time asking that one – as is the question: 'What ever happened to a **Two Day Event?**'

Hunter Trials. I do not know for the life of me what this is, except that it is completely different to either or the two above [I think] so that I can therefore say with a certain degree of confidence that *Hunter Trials* are **not** *Three* **nor** *One Day Events*. See?

Horse Trials. Sorry. Can't help you here either.

Intermediate Cross Country: Er . . .

In Hand Hunter Showing Classes. Um . . .

In Hand Novice 16.2 Under 10 Years Black and White Mountain & Moorland: Why did I ever think of doing this stupid list in the first place???

That's it, I'm afraid. Sorry I can't be of more assistance, but there again, I suppose we all have to adopt the attitude that we can all remain blissfully unaware of any of this anyway, as it won't really affect us – as long as we do our duty, turn up and discharge the tasks as aforementioned.

If you take my advice, adopt the same approach to some of the terminology *within* the event. So when, for example, you are required to stand and watch a *Dressage* event, and someone says, 'Judge 3's writer hasn't turned up'- don't begin to speculate what on earth they mean. Just accept that it means something totally alien to what *you* think it means, and then you will be OK.

And at the same event when your partner finishes whatever she is supposed to have done [you will know this because at the end of it all, she has to bow solemnly to the unseen person in the parked car] she will no doubt dismiss your pathetic attempts of smarming up to her [' . . . you did *really great!!!*' . . . and all that kind of Uriah Heap sort of stuff] with a waive of her hand and something like ' . . . no I didn't . . . I failed miserably . . . I just *couldn't* get that left diagonal to go right . . . I'm going to shoot myself . . . goodbye . . .' Just shrug your shoulders, let her go and put right out of your mind what getting a left diagonal to go right could possibly mean, and what ever you do **DON'T** suggest that next time she should try doing a triple salko.

It won't go down that well.

FUN RIDES

In addition to not wanting to go to Events, your partner will also be desperate not to go on **FUN RIDES** while at the same time being desperate *to* go on them, if you see the logic by now.

Fun Rides are apparently completely different to Events and like everything in the horsey world they are a contradiction in terms, because no one ever seems to get much fun out of them – though don't ask me to explain why, as I don't know what happens on them.

The same rules seem to apply as for Events in terms of getting to a Fun Ride. *Your* presence is mandatory, for all the same reasons – particularly as Fun Rides seem to take place in even more obscure places as Events, prompting suggestions as you trundle past the snow line in the local mountains, that it ' . . . can't *possibly* be here' – only for you to be confounded as you go round the next blind bend and clear the effects of the blizzard from your windscreen, by the sight of the same old people there again, looking *again* as though they have been camped there for fifty years or more.

On the whole, your partner will actually confess that she actually *likes* going on fun rides *actually* – excepting of course the very one you are travelling towards at that particular moment in time. *That* one is without question the *worst event* that she could ever be called upon to take part in and [yes, here we go again!!!] she must need her head looking at even contemplating going on it in the first place.

Your requirements are the same as events, too – in the nature of geographical prowess, catering skills, psychology etc etc. But what is essentially *different* about this experience from your point of view is that you stand to be abandoned for a considerable amount of time while your partner goes off doing whatever she does on the Fun Ride – and presumably getting no fun from it.

You might think this an advantage. Five hours of solitude. Left to your own devices in the wide expanses of blue yonder and all that sort of desperately sad

' I wandered, lonely, as a cloud
That floats on high o'er vale and hills . . . '

poetry suggesting sort of things.

I hate to be a complete bummer – please don't get the impression that I'm one of those sort of vacuum cleaner type people who you see at parties sometimes reminding everyone who, up to that point, were having a good time about the starving millions in China, the fluctuations in the Nikkei Dow Share Index and the endemic spread of malaria in Africa and all those wonderfully party-good-time sort of subjects. No I'm definitely not one of those, but this is, after all, a practical guide, and I must be practical at all times – so I'm afraid that your moment of euphoria at the inception of a Fun Ride is incredibly short lived.

For a start, your partner, as she gets into the saddle, once you've untangled the tack and wrestled with the girth etc etc, will take her farewells with the ominous rejoinder: 'By the way, there seems to be a bit of a problem with the hay net, can you sort it out before I get back???'

If this happens, fear the worst. It won't be as simple as it sounds and, on investigation you will very rapidly discover that the actual problem with the haynet is that it's attached to a horsebox which is just about to lose its back axle.

So you actually find yourself in the sort of poetry inducing situation which actually induces the sort of actual poetry which actually goes something like this:

> Oh I hate horses,
> Oh yes I do
> I'd love to melt them down
> And turn them into glue

All of which won't do your situation any good. What you *are* in for is the irksome business of getting someone to help you out, and perhaps find someone with a bit of knowledge about repairing back axles – yes, of course, those sort of people come ten a penny on barren hillsides in the middle of nowhere, don't they?

What *are* in abundance however, and unfortunately for you [and from here on you *know* things are going to go rapidly down hill] are plenty of non-horsey other halves.

In normal circumstances, you might welcome the opportunity of making contact with such people. After all, they are in the same mess in their lives as you are, and perhaps the occasion might lead you into some positive ground, exchanging recipes, developing useful hints you can use around the home, and maybe even cunning new patent methods for unravelling tack.

But on occasions like these, where you have a problem which is vaguely mechanical, and something to do with transport, what you *are* in imminent danger of running into is a **know-it-all mechanic**. And you do, as sure as night follows day.

He will usually be the first person you meet and will seize the opportunity you present him with loving open arms.

Not only have you provided the perfect platform for venting all that pent up emotion *he* feels about the horsey world, but it also gives him the ability to sound superior to you – even though he doesn't know any more about back axles than you do.

But nevertheless, he will *sound* very knowledgeable, and he will fire his first salvo very early on.

When you alert him to your predicament, he will be most willing to help, then as he approaches your horsebox, the tutting and shaking of the head will begin, followed by the: 'Oh, no, not one of these. I thought I'd seen the last of these back in Tobruck . . . *whatever* induced you to buy one of *these???'* in that mealy-mouthed Brummy sort of accent which all these know-it-all mechanic types seem to have, along with a name like 'Nobby'.

It's no good trying to point out that you didn't have any say at all in the decision to purchase the damn thing [see sections later on for explanation of this point] *you're* the man, so in his book, *you* are the one who's going to get all the shit and derision. Anyway, he'd be far too scared of your partner to voice his feelings to *her* – she might know *his* partner, and that would be just too much of a risk to take.

Anyway, he's enjoying this far too much to care. By now, he's into your engine, tutting and shaking the head, muttering things like 'bloody Aye-Talian engineering' and then laughing enigmatically to himself.

Then, horror of horrors, someone else, another non-horsey partner, passes by and before your can prevent it, Nobby, Mr Know-it-all-Mechanic has beckoned this total stranger to join you. And he, too, has seized this golden opportunity for a therapeutic spleen-venting-let's-have-a-laugh-at-this-twerp's-expense session.

So now you've got two know-it-alls conversing between themselves, dissecting your life, enjoying the pantomime of your increasing embarrassment, with a few 'look at that' type comments which bring the inevitable laughter and the ' you can't be serious, everyone knows that these had a left handed screw on the bi-valve relay. It's the Aye-Talian engineering . . .' comments.

Which will inevitably lead to the introduction of yet more frustrated non-horsey partners who will appear from every direction like a plague of locusts and who will crowd around your beleaguered situation with the sort of gleeful anticipation which must have been the hallmark of the front row seats around the guillotine at the time of the French Revolution.

You will watch this gathering in hapless impotency, unable to offer a comment, unable to do anything but stand by and take it all with whatever good grace you can muster, and wondering what on earth you are doing in this place, in this time, in this existence. It will continue like this until you feel that you have reached the limit of your humiliation tolerance. Then *Hey Presto!!!* it get's worse.

Out of the melee of dissecting know-it-all mechanics will emerge a figure of such dark power and magnitude as to be akin to one of those weird and eerie Black Knight figures who used to emerge, unbidden, out of the landscape, kill a few dozen yeomen, shag the birds and then disappear into the mists of time, in all those tales of yore when merry archers struck a blow 'gainst tyranny's tyrannical hand [and all that kind of stuff].

He will wear a permanent grimace, look like the sort of down-to-earth practical sort of sod who tells his children on their third birthday that there's no such person as Father Christmas, no doubt have grease up to his armpits from the sort of honest toil that mamby-pamby office workers like you would never know nothing about in your gin-and-tonic-poofter-velvet-lined-everything-coming-so-damned-bloody-easy-because-you've-got-the-sort-of-education-which-he-can-only-dream-about-but-he's-been-to-the-university-of-life-so-he's-a-ten-times-better-man-than-you'll-ever-be-so-*there*-shitface existence, and he'll be carrying a spanner. A big one. They always do.

And from the look he gives you, it is debatable whether he will set about your horsebox with it, or set about you.

Anyhow, this apparition will approach with dark foreboding, weighing the said spanner in his hand. As he walks towards you, somehow the gaggle of gloating non-horsey know-it-all-mechanics will form a natural corridor and then stand behind him in a semi-circle of admiration.

The tense atmosphere will be broken by the steely eyed look he gives you. Then, in a voice at once slow and deliberate, with each word chosen as though it has the meaning of very existence itself, heavy with an accent which could only be derived from the very soil of the country upon which you stand and laden with the sort of ominous intensity which laced Neville Chamberlain's announcement that the Second World War had just begun, he will say: 'I hear you've got axle trouble...'

In the silence which follows, you will hear your own heart beating, I can assure you.

The best that you will be able to muster will be a benign nod, indicating that he is correct, to which he will say: 'The name's Basil. I'm known in these parts

BASIL

as . . . Baz. But *you* can call me Basil. The wife tells me you need my services. What seems to be the trouble . . .'

You won't have a chance of replying. Before you have the ability to mouth the words, or even cry in anguish, 'Nobby', your original know-it-all-mechanic will eagerly step forward and offer with all the fervour of someone denouncing an under cover agent to the secret police: ' Old loppy-lugs here's got back axle trouble, Baz. Mind you, little surprise really, Baz – when you consider he's got one of these, Baz.'

Silence will once again descend. If Baz *was* a secret policeman it would be at this point that his back would stiffen perceptibly and his olive-skinned hand would move to the trigger of his pistol as he demands in his broken mid-European cum South American 'B' movie accent: *'Yourrr papers!'* But in this reality version, he will be there shaking his head and tutting to himself before turning to you, disparagingly and saying: ' How on *EARTH* could you have bought one of *THESE?* it's got a left handed screw on the bi-valve relay.'

'Yes' you will hesitantly reply, trying desperately to redeem some sort of semblance of self esteem while trying also to recall the sort of diverting statement which the 'B' movie secret agents always seem to come up with which gets them off instant arrest so that they can get out of the country in the nick of time and end the plot shagging some bimbo in a casino in the South of France. "Italian engineering I understand."

Sorry. . . you've made a fatal mistake. No bimbo and no casino for you, my friend. You're talking to Basil, remember, and he hates the very ground upon which you walk. He couldn't possibly let someone like you have an inkling of a fact which outstrips his knowledge in front of this gang of hyenas.

He will look you straight in the eye, his furrowed brow edged by the hedges of his raven hued eyebrows and say with relish: 'Bulgarian, actually – Loppy Lugs.'

Then, in the vacuum, his voice will sound like Moses coming down from the mountain with his tablets of stone. He will stand rather like Moses – or at least the Charlton Heston version – you know, big and macho, making an announcement to the semi-circle of know-it-all-mechanics which is every bit as important as: ' I have this day spoken even unto the true Gaad and he hath given me these tablets of stone.' [*why* is it that Biblical guys in those sort of films always seem to talk in a kind of 17th Century Brooklyn?]

Baz's version will go something like: ' I can solve this problem. But I need special tools. I'll be back in half an hour.'

The joyous looks of admiration on the beaming faces of the know-it-all-mechanics will be accompanied by a ripple of applause and at that he will go, and so will most of the gathering.

The only one who will stay will be Nobby and then only for about ten minutes so that he can verbally review everything which has occurred, peppering his comments with the name 'Baz' as though he were the Messiah, and occasionally calling you the aforementioned 'loppy lugs' so that he can extract the final ounces of your humiliation. Then he, too, will be gone, leaving you to reflect that next time you come on one of these Fun Rides *if*, that is, there *is* to be a next time, you must remember to bring along a tidy dose of paraquat together with a funnel so that you can forcibly pour it down Nobby's sodding throat.

As you stand bedraggled and alone beside this juggernaut of torture, you now begin to remember all those vital facts which seemed to have left you at the time you were confronting all that giggling gaggle of transport experts – like the distinct recollection which you now have of telling your partner it was a 'heap of scrap' when she was considering buying the damn thing: . . . 'it's a load of rubbish . . . look at that . . . Italian engineering . . . the axles look dodgy to me . . . it's the sort of thing the Pathe news films had in their coverage of Tobruck during the War . . .' etc etc – which of course earned you the usual replies: . . . 'what do *you* know . . . you know *nothing* about horses . . . and it's Dodo that's important in this instance . . . after all, *he's* the one who'll be travelling in it, not you!!'

There will also be another visual image in your head, of the certificate hanging on your office wall recording your Masters Degree in Advanced Automotive Engineering from the University

of Cambridge – but of course that is of little help to you when dealing with the likes of Baz who's bulky frame is now forming a distinct aspect of the distant horizon as he trudges his well selected way back towards you.

'I've made some special brackets,' he will say without any further by-your-leave. 'You'll have to help me haul 'im into position.'

What now follows is two and a half hours of excruciating pain and humiliation, accompanied by considerable grunts and groans from Baz, and silence from you as you suppress the urge to scream before the work is finally done.

Then you find yourself blubbering some sort of gratitude to Baz as he stands before your, in Moses pose again, stone faced with his hand out.

Realising what he wants you say something pathetic like:'Thanks for all your time and trouble, er... Baz... il... er... can I buy you a... er... drink??'

He will reply by looking you evilly in the eye and say:' Stuff the sodding drink. There's my time, and trouble, the special brackets, the use of my spanner, my advice, and expertise which could only have come from an Honours Degree Course at the University of Life, to say nothing about having to do a speech and usually I need a few weeks' notice practicin' in front of the mirror before I accept a speeching engagement. Shall we call it £4,000? By the way – I take credit cards.'

As you look open mouthed at him, and in a state of catatonic stupor, you will feel his hand reach inside your jacket pocket, withdraw your wallet and extract whichever is the first credit card he comes to. Then, from out of his tool kit he will take one of those electronic boxes, linked to a rather cunning little device which works off his mobile phone, and swipe your card. Then, as the machine spews out the print out, he will tear it off and hand you the counterfoil for you to sign.

You will be in such an intense state of shock that you won't be able to do anything other than his bidding, after which he will bid his good-byes with the muttered comment:' I should take it into a garage at the first opportunity. I'm no expert on axles.'

The next thing you will know as you stand there in a dazed and apoplectic state, open mouthed and still holding the torn off credit card counterfoil which flickers lazily in the breeze around you, will be a familiar voice sounding in your ear: 'We've had a *dreadful* time. He cocked up *all* the jumps and I think he's gone lame again – and the weather's been *atrocious*. You should have felt it on the top. *Absolutely bloody appalling*. Still – I suppose *you've* had it really cushy stuck in the cab with your cans of lager and newspapers. Don't you think it's time we got you an old plodder then we could go on these Fun Rides together. Still... knowing you, all you want to do is let me get on with all the work while you just sit back enjoying life.

'By the way... is the hay net fixed?'

A GENERAL GUIDE TO THE PEOPLE
YOU WILL ENCOUNTER
AND HOW TO SURVIVE THEM

Now that you've found yourself firmly embedded in the horsey world with hardly a means of escape, it is important that you are able to come to terms with the various people who populate it, and know how you are going to deal with them in order to give yourself the best possible chance of survival.

The following sections are therefore intended as an introduction if you are a fairly recent newcomer, or a reminder if you are more involved.

THE GENTRY

The Gentry are a really important element in the horsey world because they perpetuate it. If it wasn't for them, most horsey people wouldn't be interested in horses in the first place, because one of the most significant motivating forces in the whole business is being able to hobnob with the Gentry, so that instead of referring in oblique conversation to something which, say, you saw, the Earl of Baffin Land do the other day on the television, you can drop into general after dinner conversation something like: '. . . as I was only saying to Billy Baffin Land the other day. . .' Or, you can use the same ploy to get one up on polite conversation by saying something like: '. . . as Billy told me the other day. . . Billy? Oh, yes, of course you probably don't know Billy Baffin Land – oh I mean to say *The Earl of Baffin Land and Microbotinus* – do you? Have you ever seen his place? Oh, it's so *large,* it's bigger than *Swindon,* you know. . .'

The Gentry are easy to identify in the horse world. They always drive around in Range Rovers and they always arrive late – as though no event could possibly commence without their presence.

They are also extremely rich. Absolutely rolling in dosh. Rolling in so much of it in fact that they never ever refer to it – rather like the rest of us never talk about tap water.

Like tap water to us, money is always there for them. And just like we never ever bother to consider exactly how many gallons of water we flush down the bog every time we use it, the gentry never bother to contemplate how much money they have. They just content themselves in the knowledge that as far as they can remember, they own Cambridgeshire, or was it Wiltshire? Or was it Belgium? And they have shares here and there in various companies and conglomerates, without really knowing where the money goes nor how it's used, except in the safe and certain knowledge that the pile is growing somehow, somewhere, at an enormous rate. I remember hearing one once at the opening of a cardboard factory – that is, a factory which *makes* cardboard, not a factory made *of* cardboard, if you see what I mean.

73

Anyway, this git was stuck between brandies while some boring executive was droning on about the significance of this new and exciting- nay VITAL – development for the cardboard industry throughout the world and I heard him turn to his companion, who I suppose was his analyst [*financial* that is, not the other sort, even though he is obviously horsey, being Gentry] and he asked: 'What's this chap going on about cardboard for?' To which came the reply: 'That's what they make here.' To which came a very bemused look and comment: 'Do you mean to say you've tied up some of my money in . . . cardboard???' To which came a rather tied reply along the lines of ' . . . we only have 10 mill of yours invested here, and it's giving us a pretty good return, and considering that your entire pile amounts to more than the gross national product of Kenya, I don't think you'd miss it even if cardboard was to be flushed down the world-wide industrial bog . . .'

Having all this money has one effect which becomes plainly obvious whenever members of the Gentry are on public display. Because they have so much, they never bother to spend it, unless it is *absolutely necessary* – and then they spend pots of it.

So when they need a four wheel drive vehicle to take them here and there to horse shows and the like, it's always the top of the range Range Rover which gets dusted off. But if you expect top of the range outfits to suit the top of the range Range Rover, then you will be sorely disappointed. Because out of the top of the range Range Rover will spill an odd assortment of people clad in the sort of clothes everyone else buys from a downmarket version of the Oxfam Shop.

So if you are at a horse event and encounter someone who looks like he's just sold his last copy of the Big Issue, *don't* engage him in conversation and *CERTAINLY DON'T* talk down to him, because he's more than likely to be the very same Billy Baffin Land aka *The Earl of Baffin Land and Microbotinus*, in the flesh.

Which brings me to indicate a few ground rules on dealing with the Gentry, with whom you are bound to rub shoulders as you make your troubled and turbulent way through the horsey world.

THE INITIAL CONTACT

As I have already said, *never* start a conversation with them. *They* don't require you to, so you will do yourself no good at all if you attempt it.

Wait to be spoken to by *them*. This might not happen for some time but if your partner is seriously into the horsey world [and let's face it they are all barmy enough to get deeper and deeper enmeshed in its tentacles] there will inevitably come a time when you will become sufficiently juxtaposed to a Gentry personage to warrant an address from him/her [though be careful in deciding *which* gender you are dealing with – as most of the female gentry look and behave very much like the males, particularly when they get older].

When this happens, it will probably be either in the form of a command such as: ' Go and give those gels a hend will you' or an interrogation such as: ' . . . and what do we hev har?' [meaning *you* of course].

In either event, you must remember that the person who has just spoken to you lives in a completely different time to you. To them, it is still 1868, when everything was in order in the Empire, the fuzzy-wuzzies knew their place, Johnny Foreigner didn't bother us that much and good honest working stock knew that their role in life was to work their bollocks off day and night with only a few hours off on Christmas Day when they could go to Church to thank Heaven for their place in the world, to amass more and more and more wealth for . . . well, the Gentry.

So you are still servant class and they are still ruling class [which, in fact, they still are, but we'll come on to that a little later on].

While you might think you have a reasonably good standing in society – you probably think you made it when you became Sales Director, or a Partner in a leading firm of Architects, or Chief Administrator or something like that; and you probably think that having a smart address in the better side of town and running two cars are symbols of some sort of achievement, remember to the Gentry, that means nothing at all.

They probably own your company, though they probably don't know that. They might even own the firm that makes your cars and the one that built your house, and they will also no doubt own the very ground upon which your sainted acre resides.

None of this will necessarily emerge unless you annoy them, in which case you will be rapidly reminded that a variety of people with whom they are intimately connected and who all seem to be sporting stupid sounding names like 'Poggy', 'Tiggy', 'Stinky', 'Fruity' and the like turn out to be *your* Chairman, The Lord Chancellor, the Chairman of the Local Health Authority, the Archbishop of Canterbury and so on and so forth. And of course they will never fail to point that out to you as a kind of opening salvo, with the promise of infinitely worse to come if you persist.

So be warned.

Make sure, therefore, that when addressed, you respond correctly. If it is the command you have been given, make sure that you act upon it diligently and swiftly, and ***don't expect a reward***. These people have to be reminded from time to time that the average person actually gets *paid* for doing their every day job, so for the odd command on an open field they will certainly not expect to reward you with thanks – though the odd one may forget himself and reach in his pocket for a penny tip in order to give himself that warm satisfying feeling at maintaining the differentials between the master and servant.

If it is the question mode you encounter for the first time, then you must be polite and immediately try to establish a connection, such as in the following:

[the Gentry Person] 'What air you?'

[You] ' Jimmy Squib [here put in your own name of course, otherwise it will become far too confusing to the Gentry Person who will rapidly reach the conclusion that everyone in the servant class of the horsey world is called Jimmy Squib] Sir.'

The addition of 'Sir' is very important and highly recommended because it reassures the Gentry Person that you are just as keen as he/she is in maintaining those all too important differentials. [You] 'I'm married to Helen Squib – who won this event last year. I think you presented the Cup to her if I'm not mistaken.'

At this point, you will know you've done well if the Gentry Person nods benignly and knowingly, looks wistfully into the air and says something like:

[Gentry Person] 'Oh, yarse...Helen Squid [yes, he got the name wrong but *don't* point that out]. Av course. Ay remember...Av course. How es she? Es she well?

[You] 'Yes, Sir. Very well indeed.'

[Gentry Person] 'Good...remember me to her will you?

He will then grab some other finger who happens to be passing by and say:

[Gentry Person] ' Booby, hev you met Bernie Squid – married to Harriet who won the cup hare 10 yars ego...'

At which point he will beat a hasty retreat because he will be fully aware that you know that he has absolutely no recollection of your partner, and certainly can't remember presenting any cup to anyone last year, as by that time the general level of gin had long overtaken the red corpuscles threading through what was left of his brain.

However, you can rest assured that you will have come out of this encounter unscathed and not without a little congratulation, and you will be ready to move onwards and upwards on your journey of survival.

Which brings me to my next guidepost on the way: **THE GENTRY**

GENTRYSPEAK

Only a moment's encounter with the Gentry [as I think some of your will have realised by now] will reveal that they all speak a completely different English to the rest of us, and you won't get very far in your quest for survival if you don't understand a few basics regarding pronunciation.

But one very important word of warning here: **DON'T** whatever you do try to talk Gentryspeak yourself. You will fail miserably, because quite frankly you lack the breeding [or is it *in*breeding] and all you will end up with is a pale imitation of Gentryspeak which will not only sound like a lampoon to them, and therefore bring on a diatribe of reminders as to who they know in high places and who would do you and your career severe damage, but will also sound to other non-Gentry people that you are comitting the cardinal sin of trying to **Ape the Gentry,** and, at worst could even lead to you being classified as one of THOSE WHO WOULD LIKE TO BE THE GENTRY BUT HAVEN'T GOT THE MONEY of which more anon.

Anyhow, on the strictest understanding that you will only use this little lexicon as a guide for fathoming out what on earth they are talking about, let's press on.

As a general rule of thumb, Gentryspeak uses vowel sounds which are one vowel before that which is written – so if you have a word with a predominantly 'o' or 'ou' sound *as written,* Gentryspeak will *sound* that word with a predominantly 'i' sound.

So: 'Boy Scout', for example *as written.*

Becomes:' Bi Skite' *as spoken.*

There are some exceptions of course. A predominantly 'a' sound takes on an 'e" sound: 'Have', for example, becomes 'Hev', and a hard 'o' sound becomes 'or': 'Across' in this case, becoming 'Acrorse'.

This can lead to some thrilling combinations on surprisingly simple words. Take 'About', for example, which becomes 'Ebite', and 'Around' becomes 'Erind'. And even more complex words become dazzling: 'Absolutely' for instances becomes 'Ebsoilitelee'.

So armed with these general pointers [or should it be *pinters*] you can now see that if a Gentryperson in interrogatory mode points distantly across a field to some distant figures and enquires: 'Hev thise Bi Skites tined arind end air they gying acrorse thet feeld iver thair?' you will know exactly what he or she is saying. Though for goodness sake, *don't even think* about replying: 'Ebsoilitelee'.

Another aspect of Gentryspeak which is important to understand at this point is that often at horsey events, they will talk complete gibberish to each other.

You will often find two of them discussing the day's events thus: 'Et's ebsoilitelee *wanderful* may deer . . . ebsoilitelee wanderful . . . harses . . . sheep . . . all thise dare cheps with kettle . . . end et's si grin . . . si grin . . . thes gress . . . si grin . . . harses end pinees . . . end et's si grin . . .'

Usually this will be accompanied by wild gesticulating, as though one of them is just about to explode.

This is not as serious as it might seem . . . It is generally caused by a combination of factors including; 1. These are two horsey people and therefore they are barmy. 2. They are Gentry and therefore have so much dosh that they never really needed to learn how to string together words into sentences like the rest of us [remember such people often *own* the University which gave them their degrees, so they didn't have to bother actually *attending* the place nor *learning* anything like the rest of us] 3. Whatever brain cells were present in the past have long succumbed to frequent and systematic dosing in gin.

However, do not linger in the vicinity of such an event, in some sort of gormless rubber necking exercise. If you do, you could attract their attention, and they may interpret that your behaviour is threatening. You will know that you are entering the danger zone if one of them breaks off the diatribe and eyes you with a steely glance followed by the eternal menacing question: "Ken ay halp yu?" This is a prelude to a broadside across your bows such as 'Ay own the Medland Benk, do yu benk thar?"

If this happens you could be in deep trouble and my advice is to get out of there as quickly as possible.

THOSE WHO WOULD LIKE TO BE THE GENTRY BUT HAVEN'T GOT ANY MONEY

Now we come on to perhaps the most interesting – and certainly the most hilarious – bunch you will ever have to encounter in the horse world. That sad group of sad people sadly trying to make out that they are members of the Gentry but failing miserably mainly because they don't so much own the 'Medland Benk' as have a rather larger than usual overdraft in it.

Like you and me they have ordinary jobs – or at least some of them have – with ordinary salaries, but unlike you and me, they spend all of it, not just on horses, but also on the whole business of trying to make out that they are Gentry. Consequently, they have nothing left for such luxuries as food, electricity, heat and light, and a roof over their heads in the winter time.

Their big mistake is that they delude themselves into thinking that having pots of dosh means that you have to sport the best of everything – but as we have already seen, *real* Gentry only spend pots of dosh when it is *absolutely necessary*, such as purchasing the top of the range Range Rover. For the rest of the time, the family millions cook quietly away in safe investments like cardboard factories, making even more family millions without anyone having really to do anything.

Which brings us to an important rule of thumb for differentiating between *real* Gentry and **THOSE WHO WOULD LIKE TO BE GENTRY BUT HAVEN'T GOT ANY MONEY.**

As we have already discussed, when they arrive at horsey events, *real* Gentry spill out of the top of the range Range Rovers wearing something out of the Oxfam shop. On having done so, they make a beeline for the first hip flask glistening in the sunshine, and with terrific sighs of relief swig down its contents in one fell swoop. Such an action is necessary because the gin level can often reach a dangerously low ebb in the old metabolism during the drive from the stately pile to the horse event, on account of the fact that, as the Gentry don't actually *own* Police Forces any more because of the disturbing and completely unnecessary rise of totally out-of-order upstarts who believe that the law should actually apply to *everyone* [yes even those in the same Masonic Lodge as the Chief Constable] these days they tend to have that same fear as anyone else of the little plastic machine administered at the side of the road by totally upstart young whippersnapper PC's who should muckle down and respect their betters rather than running them into the local nick when they're found to be fifteen times over the drink drive limit. [I'm quite convinced that the first people most of the Gentry would hang if they ever succeeded in their often declared aims of bringing back capital punishment, sending all the immigrants back home on the banana boats, giving all homeless a sound public thrashing, and telling disabled people to stop wingeing and get some backbone, would be the aforementioned Coppers – however]

THOSE WHO WOULD LIKE TO BE GENTRY BUT HAVEN'T GOT ANY MONEY, can easily be spotted because they are wearing the very latest in designer tweeds, and what is more:

You don't see them arrive. This is either because they don't have a vehicle of their own [because it was either repossessed or it was sold to pay for the hire of a penguin outfit so that they could go to the Hunt Ball] or, if they *do* have a vehicle, it will be some sort of beaten up wreck, with plenty of filler on the wings and at least one door which is a different

THE GENTRY 'WANNABE'.

colour from the other three on account of the fact that the scrap yard only had that particular colour in stock – and will therefore have been parked far away to avoid embarrassment.

If you were to question them as to what vehicle they were currently running around in, you will be told somewhat dismissively that they are: 'currently grounded', on account of a 'prang'. Along with: 'Bit of a bitch actually. . . rather curtailed my activities . . . have had to rely on a few chums to give me a lift' Or ' . . . have had to make do with an old crate I picked up for a fiver . . . '

It's only after you've known the person for about six months, and the 'crate' is still being run around in, do you begin to suspect the validity of this version of events.

Another pointer to look out for is the non-invitation.

You will never be invited back to their place – because they probably haven't got one.

A large number of this fraternity float about from one hard pressed long suffering acquaintance to another, outstaying their welcome by several months or even years in some extreme examples, until they are finally dumped on the streets, by measures which can be bordering on the desperate such as the acquaintance volunteering for permanent residency on the moon.

Another good pointer is the vague reference to employment which these people will give you. Often in the course of general conversation it is normal to enquire as to the employed status of the person you are talking to. If you are confronted by an impeccably dressed individual who is failing miserably in his or her attempts at Gentryspeak, and who did not seem to have arrived in any vehicle that day, and who seems to be getting a considerable amount of dirty and hateful looks from someone introduced to you as their 'best chum', then you can get final confirmation that he or she is one of this fraternity by asking the simple and direct question: 'And what do you do for a living?'

The answer you will get can be defined easily.

The most popular one is this:

'Oh . . . I'm in between careers at the moment . . . just taking a rain check on life and all that sort of thing . . . '

Which means: ' I am a permanently unemployed layabout who prefers to spend all of my time and benefit money on hobnobbing with the Gentry in the hope that I might find out one day how to get my hands on all that dosh.'

In this respect, they *do* share something in common with the *real* Gentry in that neither group actually *works* for a living.

Sometimes, if they happen to be *in* employment [often, it has to be said, because the Social Security people have finally come to the end of their tether and *insisted* that this time it is a job *or else*] you are given a vague suggestion – the vagueness deliberately chosen to conceal the mundane nature of the actual job.

Thus: 'Oh, I'm in retailing . . .'

Means: 'I work in a shop'

Or: 'I'm in Stocks and Shares'

Means: 'I try to sell life insurance'

Or: 'I'm in interior design'

Means: ' I'm a painter and decorator's mate'

Or – and this is one of the *best:*
        'I'm in the meat business'

Means: 'I lump dead carcasses around the frozen meat cash and carry'

Similarly when one of these people shouts out in a voice intended for everyone to hear that: ' Look, I can't hang around here too long, I've got 500 head of sheep which need shearing in the morning...' those of you who are fairly new to this sort of thing might immediately jump to the conclusion that this finger is some sort of landed Gent. Those of you who have been around for perhaps a little longer will know that in fact he's a farm *labourer,* and it is *he* who will be rising with the lark to do the shearing.

I could go on, but by now I guess you've got the picture.

Without question the most endearing feature of these people is that *you never actually see them ride a horse.*

Horsey they are most definitely. They tell you that all the time. But the actual *evidence* of their horse riding prowess is in the same realms of vagueness as their employment status.

There are plenty of references as to what they have done in the past, of course. They were out hunting only last week, for instance *and* they were at the South Partington Pakistani Test Match Headingly Edgbaston The Oval Lords Trent Bridge Old Trafford Hunter Trials, but had a little bit of bother at the 12th.

And there are plenty of references to what they are *going to do,* as in: 'Are you going to Upper Letchworth on Wednesday, I'm supposed to be taking out one of Billy Baffin Land's nags for a trial, but with this vehicle problem I could really do with a lift . . . do you think you could see your way to . . . etc etc etc.'

But the *actual* day when you are there to witness the said person *actually* on the back of an *actual* horse never seems to *actually* arrive, *actually*. And were you to take matters into the realms of stealth warfare and turn up on Wednesday at Upper Letchworth unannounced just to witness the performance with Billy Baffin Land's nag, you can be sure that the said person with the said nag will not be there.

Sidling up to the person in question at the next gathering, you might think yourself pretty clever by casually dropping out in conversation something like: ' . . . by the way I went to Upper Letchworth last Wednesday, and I looked out for you, but you didn't seem to be there . . . '

If you thought you were being clever, put away your smug grin because you will get an immediate response without even the hint of a pause along the lines of: ' . . . oh, yes . . . I know . . . it was a real bummer . . . the bloody thing went lame, didn't it . . . ruined the whole day . . . '

You see, these people are adept at getting themselves out of troubles like this. After all, they have had plenty of time in the dole queues to develop a whole subculture which protects them and which manifests itself in the almost hysterical attempts at charisma which oozes from their every pore.

When first you meet one of them, for example, you will of course be properly introduced by your partner [this is an obvious pre-requisite of the horsey world and particularly of the surreal world of **THOSE WHO WOULD LIKE TO BE GENTRY BUT HAVEN'T GOT ANY MONEY**, because they know that no self respecting Gentry person would have anything to do with you in a social situation unless proper introductions had been made containing some sort of connection to someone else that they have never heard of but in a social situation they would profess to be a bosom pal] such as: ' . . . Adrian, have you met my husband Jimmy Squib?' [Surely, she can't finally be introducing you to *that* Adrian, can she???] . . . you will immediately receive a glance from head to toe which gives the **PERSON WHO WOULD LIKE TO BE GENTRY BUT HASN'T GOT ANY MONEY** a moment in order to assess the threat you could or could not pose, hurl a salvo at you in the form of a look which could be interpreted as 'What on *Earth* is it standing before me?' before uttering the immortal:

'UGGGGH'

pronounced in a fashion which is almost like throwing up.

Then with you firmly put into context, the hand is extended in a commanding sort of way, followed by 'pleased to meet you, I'm sure.' [Those of you who have already been through this little party piece will have observed that the hand was wiped on the trousers after it made contact with yours in a sort of rather-disparaging-and-not-very- subtle-attempt-at-trying-to-conceal-what-he-was-actually-doing sort of way, as if he had just shaken hands with the backside of a bullfrog]

This is then followed by the general interrogation: 'Do *you* ride?' said in the sort of tone which suggest that the question really being asked is: 'Don't tell me that a pathetic wimp like *you* could even consider getting on the back of a noble creature such as a 16.2 thoroughbred stallion, like I do every day of the year . . . actually

To which, you will of course reply: ' No I don't'

This is immediately followed by a nod [usually in a sort of pseudo-military style, probably perfected after constant practice watching those Victorian reconstruction dramas about the Hussars that are so popular on the box – you can almost see the Navy blue uniform with the scrambled egg on the shoulders standing before you] which could be taken as one of admonition as in: 'There, I was right, you *are* a pathetic wimp, just as I thought.' Or it is more likely to be one of great relief as in: 'Thank *God* this person cannot possibly be a threat.

This will then be followed either by a vague look into space in an attempt to find someone else to talk to – after all, if you *were* a threat then this bloke would want to skiddaddle as quickly as possible and as you are *not,* then you have already been placed into context and therefore there is no further need to talk to you.

If, on the other hand, there is no immediate handle to grab this pratt away from you, he then has to spend a few agonising moments in conversation. As you have already proved to be no threat, he will seek solace and a consoling reassurance of re-establishing his superior position by indulging himself in the sport of talking down to you, in order to make the passage of time a little more interesting.

This is when you will get all the bullshit about employment etc but then he will inevitably steer the conversation in the direction of something which allows him the ability to demonstrate his well practised [in front of the mirror, no doubt] ability to demonstrate just how superior he is to a slimy little weevil like you who has had the audacity to even attempt to engage a Captain in the Royal Victorian Order of Antediluvian [Only Got Blackballed Once by the Masons But I'm Still Trying, Oh Why Oh Why Won't Some Lodge at Least Give Me the Chance To Demonstrate that I Could Be A Faithful and Diligent Mason!!!!] Regiment of Hussars, like him.

The likeliest subject will be wine.

It follows that these people are wine experts. Being a wine expert suggests some cultural credibility, some sort of pedigree upbringing, and as very few people actually *know* what they are talking about when it comes to wine [and who really cares anyway? It's only another means of getting pissed after all!] they can easily get away with talking complete and utter gibberish but at the same time sound very knowledgeable and important.

Ironically, you will more often than not give this Gay Hussar the intro. As you have absolutely nothing in common with him other than the fact that you both have glasses in your hands, reference will inevitably be made to the contents, but he will allow you to make the first move. This is to enable him to establish an immediate superiority.

You will say something like: 'Nice wine this.'

To which he will reply: 'Oh, do you think so? It tastes quite *dreadful*. Like something you get out of a supermarket. What's more, it tastes vaguely *New World* – and *everyone* knows that the New World wallahs couldn't produce a wine to save their lives...'

If you then follow up with something like: 'You sound as though you know a thing or two about wine...' you will give him the perfect opportunity to sound humble which is an important element in trying to ape the Gentry.

After all, **THOSE WHO WOULD LIKE TO BE GENTRY BUT HAVEN'T GOT ANY MONEY** want more than anything else to be like all those Gentry people from the past who got all the kudos for liberating areas of France in the Second World War [along with about 200,000 or so everyday guys who didn't pick up the royalties from being played by Jack Hawkins in the film version].

Have you ever noticed, by the way, that when they replay the interviews in those deadly dull 'Major General Basil 'Bonzo' Utterly-Boring Reminisces On His Part In Killing Lots of Japs And Jerries, in interview with Trevellian St-Peters, Emeritus Professor of Modern Warfare at the University of Scunthorpe' sort of programmes on the telly, the Gentry bloke will never shrink from the opportunity of saying something like: 'et worze rarely nathing rarely... jest dying may jorb...'

He's being *humble* – because it isn't really the done thing in Gentry circles to be seen to be taking credit. *That* is self evident and understood from the outset, because *he's* a Gentry bloke and would naturally have all the credit heaped on him, and therefore it needs no further elaboration nor acknowledgement – particularly as 'Bonzo' was no doubt sipping pink gin back in the Officers' Mess about 40 miles away from the action while nonentities like ex-car worker 'Sapper' Brian Barnsley was winning his posthumous VC getting shot to pieces on the front line.

Being humble also has another advantage in that it also brings with it further adulation as in:' How on earth could he say such a think, after *all* that he *did*. This man must be *superhuman* – I *must* go out and increase his royalties income by buying his book of personal memoirs which he wrote at the time from the perilous situation of Divisional HQ during the fiercest fighting.'

Anyhow, that is what you will get from this **PERSON WHO WOULD LIKE TO BE GENTRY BUT HASN'T GOT ANY MONEY.** To your inquiry regarding his prowess as a wine expert he will say something along the lines of: 'Oh ay know a few ord thangs. Ay dabble, but mostly ay beleev in heving a *ruddy gud wayne shipper.* Just take his advice. Thet's may mottoe. By the way, hev you sempled those new young waynes coming in frorm the Ardeche? My wine shipper tells me they will be *spectecular* in a few yars tayme, and they've come in et a snip of a prayce, almost ridiculouse, bordering on the ludicrous en fect — three fifty a case — so they are rarely worth laying dine at the moment.'

Several things can be drawn from this statement. First of all, the reference to the wayne -sorry *wine* shipper [let's get out of this ludicrous lingo once and for all!!!] (aka 'Off Licence' to you and me) is all important because it is his attempt to establish a firm differential. Normal people go to the shops, hence we get our wine from a high street wine shop or supermarket. The Gentry don't go to the shops. After all, if you own Wiltshire, then what's the point of wasting your time visiting your holdings every day? And anyway, if you did, the shopkeepers might engage you in conversation and then you will have to be civil to them. So for the Gentry the shops come to them in a fashion which never really involves them. It's all part of the process of things always being available, always being there.

So it is important if you want to give off the impression that you are vaguely Gentry that you leave the feeling that *you* likewise don't go to the shops — hence you have a 'wine shipper'. The term also implies that this man, whoever he is, is involved in some sort of overseas dealings *just for you.* That in some far off distant and exotic land, some sort of deal is being struck by some guy in a Panama hat and white jacket, and the precious nectar is being carefully crated and carried by native bearers to a wooden vessel with three tall masts which then sets sail across the perilous tides to end up in you own personal 'wayne' cellar.

He has also been careful to establish a foreign name from a region that you probably didn't get to when on your two weeks' motor caravan tours of France in those heady, far off days, when you could actually *afford* such things. That way he can get away with referring to a French region which sounds vaguely distant and exotic.

Then, of course, there is the reference to the 'case', which again establishes a differential between those who buy wine by the case (i.e. 12 bottles at a time) and by the bottle (i.e. from the supermarket shelves).

However, he has made one howling error. In his desperate need to establish his superiority, he has had to refer to cost as in: 'It's only 350 for the case' (i.e. at a price which the likes of your couldn't *possibly* afford) but of course he has carefully left out the *actual* currency. It's 350 what? Reticulated Newt Droppings? Well sticky pages from some rough book?

You may of course assume that he means £350, in which case he may feel that he has achieved something — though of course he has carefully phrased what he said. He never actually said that he had bought a case.

But nevertheless he has confirmed once and for all that he is not Gentry and never could be. *Real* Gentry never refer to costs at any time. Buying things is not an activity in which they personally indulge, so they have no idea what things cost. Agents and retainers see to things like that.

Furthermore, did you notice that in the attempts at Gentryspeak, only certain words were in the sainted tongue. For the rest, the odd vernacular accent seemed to be creeping in far too much, revealing the fact that this finger more than likely went to West Bromwich Comprehensive rather than Eton.

And come to think of it, that thing which was sitting on the top of his bonce like a Cheshire cat looked suspiciously like one of those toupees that are a different colour on top from the real hair poking out from underneath.

Anyhow, after this briefest of encounters, you will be relieved from any further sparring by the arrival of someone else who will be quickly grabbed by the **PERSON WHO WOULD LIKE TO BE GENTRY BUT HASN'T GOT ANY MONEY,** who will say something like, 'Hey, Winky you old barstud, hev you met Jimmy Squid [yes, he got it *wrong* as well but don't prolong matters. Just let this dickhead go as quickly as possible] he's Helen's non-horsey other half.

THE KNOW-IT-ALL HORSEY PEOPLE

Next down in the horsey pecking order are the Know-it-Alls. These form the main bulk of the horsey world, so it is vitally important that you try to come to terms with these more than any other grouping.

Very quickly after you have entered the wonderful world of horses, you will understand that *everyone* knows *everything* there is ever likely to be known about horses. Everyone is an expert. Including your partner.

It therefore also follows in this all-knowing, all-seeing, environment that from everybody's point of view, *nobody* else knows *anything* about horses – or at the very least has *completely the wrong opinion*. The *only* people who know *everything* is *everybody*. But at any one encounter, *everyone else* knows nothing, other than, that is, *everyone else* who doesn't happen to be there at the time. See?

If you are still confused – and by golly you shouldn't be by now, you've been living with this sort of logic for long enough, remember – let me give you an example which will make things a little clearer.

Your first introduction will, naturally enough, be via your partner.

As you stand yet again, alone, bewitched, bedraggled and bewildered in some open field, wondering what the cobbler will be charging you *this* week and whether you can afford the dry cleaning bill for your best suit [putting it another way: would it be *too* much to ask that you could have it back for an hour or two so that you can wear it for your latest vital negotiations with the Bank Manager, so that you will be able to clear a number of pressing and mounting creditor claims: like the dry cleaner for instance. It *should* be OK. After all, he *did* allow you to do this last month!!] your partner will be approached by another member of the horsey fraternity [or should it be *sorority?*]

She, like your partner, will be ponced up in jods and hacking jacket and sporting the latest in designer bone domes and carrying a whip [they *all carry* whips, for use *they* say, on the horse. It's a case of *'pull the other one'* if you ask me, so I strongly advise you at all times to stay well clear and out of whip range].

From the moment this person arrives, you will know that your partner has never set eyes on her before in her life. You will know this because they will greet each other as though they have been bosom pals for years.

It will start with some sort of: 'Well . . . *hello there!!!'* sort of welcome from the visiting horsey person.

'Hello!' your partner will muster in a sort of I-know-I've-never-met-you-nor-seen-hide-nor-hair-of-you-before-but-I-know-I-can't-admit-that-in-front-of-Jimmy-because-I'm-supposed-to-know-*everyone*-in-the-horsey-world-so-I'll-make-out-we're-bosom-pals sort of voice.

'How old is he now?' the other horsey person will say [pointing to the *horse*, stupid, not *you*]'

'Ten'

'How's his laminitis?' [to the uninitiated this might seem to confirm that this person *does* know your partner after all, but as we all know that *all* horses make a point of maintaining their laminitis levels at all times, it is irrelevant]

'Oh . . . you know . . .'

'Yes . . . quite . . . you *must* try Dr Crippen's Special Cyanide with Hollyhocks, Bracken, Ragwort and Added Arsenic Compound, it is *simply perfect* for laminitic horses – like him . . . I take it you haven't come *acrorse* it yet???'

'No . . . can't say that I have. I tend to use Sweeney Todd's Special Slaughter House with Deadly Nightshade, Semtex and Nerve Gas Extracts . . . but thanks for the tip . . . I'll certainly give it a try . . . if *ever* I come across it . . .'

At that point, the other person, thinking that she has done enough to demonstrate that she knows more about horses than your partner, will have no further need to remain, and will slope off to someone else she can harangue.

Meanwhile, your partner will mutter to herself: 'Dr Crippen's . . . DR CRIPPEN'S!!! . . . *everyone* knows that that stuff is a waste of time. Trish tried it on Squeeky, and look what happened to him – fallen withers!!! And Mrs Harris used it once on Booby last winter and she had to have the Vet out twice a day. Had to have him in a Hackamore Twin Forearm Smash Double Axle Downhill Cresta Run Bit for the rest of the season.'

If you were stupid enough to join the debate here with some sort of comment like: 'Why didn't you tell *her* that then?', you will immediately find yourself in negative land again.

"Why should I tell *her* anything. Anyone can *see* she doesn't know a thing about horses. She'd obviously *never heard* of Sweeney Todd's. I mean *everyone* has *sworn* by Sweeney Todd's for *years*. It's the *only thing* which is *really effective* against laminitis. I mean, *Tony* put me onto it originally. And the one thing which Farriers *know* about is *laminitis*. What's more you can *tell* that woman knows *nothing* about horses from what she was wearing – from her safety helmet to her jods . . . all the wrong stuff.'

So you can see from this simple encounter that while the other person *thought* she knew everything there was to know about horses, actually she knew *nothing at all* – and it is your partner who actually knows *everything*, along with Trish, Mrs Harris and Uncle Tom Cobbly and All – *all*, that is, except whoever she was who had just demonstrated her crass ignorance of the whole horsey world.

This sort of encounter is fairly common, and is given added weight by an ever increasing assortment of very difficult terms which sound very complicated but actually mean very little.

For example: ' I've got Bonky on micronised barley at the moment . . .'

If you were daft enough to ask something like: 'What advantages does that give you?' you will get in return: "well . . . i t's . . . er . . . *micronised* . . . you . . . er . . . don't appear to know *much* about horses, do you?"

You will then reply something like: 'No I don't'

To which you will suddenly get the realisation, as this person loses all interest in you and is walking away: 'Oh . . . of course . . . aren't you Helen Squib's *non-horsey other half?*'

To which you will hear at your side, a low muttering from your partner: 'micronised barley . . . MICRONISED BARLEY . . . *everyone* knows that's a complete and utter con . . . *never* works . . . Connie tried it on Bubbles last winter . . . etc etc.'

In this august and all knowing world of horses, it is therefore strongly advisable *never* to voice an opinion. After all, you would *never* propose to know *anything* about horses, and everyone who knows *everything* about them actually knows *nothing*. So if you think it is worth trying to get a word into any conversation be it at an event, standing in the middle of a field, at a social gathering or whatever, you are on a hiding to nothing.

For example, in a conversation about Bits, you may feel that you had gleaned enough information on the grapevine to have your ten penneth, and interject with something like: 'Dodo seems to go best in a Malawian Transvestite How's-Yer-Father Greenstick Fracture . . .'

You will be offering this opinion in good faith and in the naive belief that your voice will be in the first instance heard – and therefore your actual presence will be acknowledged [this is obviously debatable anyway] and that secondly, what you have said is given due consideration.

If you pass the first hurdle –i.e. the conversation actually pauses and doesn't continue as though you never said anything in the first place – you will certainly not get past the second. You will know this when the rest of the people present dissolve into uncontrollable laughter.

At first you won't understand, and probably think someone has cracked a joke. Then the realisation will creep over you that it is *you* who is the source of everyone's side splitting merriment.

The first person to splutter into decipherable language will try as earnestly as they can to put you on the right tracks: ' . . . a Malawian Transvestite How's-Yer-Father Greenstick Fracture is a *Hacakmore* derivative, Jimmy, so I think it is *highly unlikely* that Dodo would be seen dead in one of those.'

If you try soldiering on with some sort of rearguard action along the lines of: ' But Helen *always* said that he did best in a Malawian Transvestite How's-Yer-Father Greenstick Fracture . . .' you will not only find the ground taken from under your very feet, but also realise that by now you have strayed into mega-negative territory, when your partner enters the debate: ' . . . no . . . Jimmy . . . *what* I actually *said* . . . if you'd only been *listening* to me is that Dodo does best in a *Sri Lankan Trans-Siberian*.'

To which the rest of the gaggling band of Know-it-Alls will breath a collective sigh of relief and collectively say: '*Exactly*'.

On the way home, your partner, when she finally deigns to speak to you, will offer something like: 'How *could* you show me up in front of all those people.'

To which you will offer: 'But I thought that's what you had said . . . I was only trying to be helpful . . .'

To which she will offer: 'Well, you're *all* wrong anyway. Dodo has never been happier since I put him in a Blue Moroccan Sherbert Dip-Dab Umbrella Snaffle – and *no-one* knows him better than me!!!'

So in a nutshell, my advice with all these people is:

DON'T SAY ANYTHING AT ANY TIME, unless you find yourself in a no-win situation in which case, just accept the inevitable ridicule, humiliation, negative points and general chastisement which you will suffer and then, as you lick your wounds in the dark corner of your lonely room, comfort yourself with the eternal endearing, and indeed, from your point of view **necessary** thought, that . . . well . . . They *are* all barmy.

There does remain, however, one final group which deserves mention, even though it is in the minority.

I refer of course to

You will have noticed from day one that the horsey world in the main tends to be populated by women. Those men who seem to be around as you make your own tawdry journey, seem to decorated with the same lame dog expression that you have most of the time, so they are obviously in the same non-horsey-other-half situation as you. For the rest, there are those who are either driving beaten up old station wagons, and are therefore Vets, or, are showing off their latest Rolex Lobster watches on their wrists, and are therefore Farriers.

However, from time to time, you will encounter

These are individuals who are in the horsey world for one reason and one reason only. They differ from the rest. They patrol, shark like through the horsey world in search of one thing and one thing only. I refer of course to

From their point of view it is a matter of how much rumpy-pumpy can be achieved in any one microsecond, and with how many of the band of know-it-all horsey women who happen to be hanging around at any one time.

The horsey world, of course, gives such people the perfect pervert package – loads of women in tight clingy jods, with whips and starched white shirts and uniforms and *equipment* all made out of *iron and steel and leather . . . loads and loads of big wobbly bottoms, and BOOBS FLAPPING ABOUT AS THEY ESCAPE FROM TIGHTLY FITTING BODICES . . . AND BOOTS . . . LEATHER BOOTS . . . ALL SHINY AND THEN COVERED IN MUCK AND MUD . . . SOME WITH HIGH HEELS . . . AND LOADS AND LOADS OF MUCK ALL OVER THE PLACE . . . ALL THOSE RUMPS AND BOOBS AND . . . WOBBBBBLING . . . AND . . .* 0 0 0 0 0 .... **YE**👓👓👓 .... **YE**👓👓👓 .... **YE**👓👓👓👓👓👓👓👓👓

er . . . oh yes . . . Now where was I?

You have no doubt wondered when you go to events, what those strange little green cabins are, dotted around the field. You will assume that they are portable loos, but in fact they are portable cold shower blocks to help calm these **MEN** down when the going gets a little too hot to handle.

Anyway, the first indication that you have encountered such a bloke is the measure of his dress. The Gentry, as we have discussed, turn up in something cast off by the Oxfam Shop. **THOSE WHO WOULD LIKE TO BE THE GENTRY BUT HAVEN'T GOT ANY MONEY,** turn up in the best possible clothes, but almost always, these will be everyday clothes, not horseykit. To turn up at events wearing horseykit might raise the spectre of them being asked to *ride a horse* and this would never do, of course.

So if you come across a bloke *wearing* horseykit in a sort of shark like manner, he will undoubtedly be one of these **MEN**. Further inspection will confirm this.

His jods will be cut particularly tightly around his groin region, with the suspicion, in your mind at least, of extra padding in the same area. The boots will be particularly spick and span, and the peak of the bonedome will incorporate something which you suspect could well be a viewfinder.

Further confirmation will come when your partner comes on to the scene. He will ignore you, and concentrate all his attention on her – particularly, you will notice, her *rear* end. It will seem to attract him – and his viewfinder – like a magnet. To the extent that as he talks to her, he will seem to be constantly angling to get *behind* her.

And then he will start making *remarks* about the aforementioned part of your partner's anatomy, such as:

'It was a vision of loveliness as I saw you ride Mrs Squib – or may I call you *Helen?* I have never seen such composure and control. If I might be so bold, your horse's rump seemed to be so much in harmony with your own . . . the way you *gave him his head* made me wonder whether you might be disposed to . . .'

At that moment, he will sort of vaguely realise that you are somewhere around, and possibly that this might not be the right sort of time to make the sort of proposal that he was getting around to, so he will withdraw with the hurried: ' . . . oh . . . sorry. . . must fly, I've just seen Billy Baffin Land over there and there's something I've just *got* to tell him . . . bye . . .' Then, as an afterthought, he might turn to you in haste and say something like: 'By the way, old boy, I think your wife's got a *stupendous bum* . . . bet you keep *her* in trim, eh?' With a sort of Terry-Thomas inflection you could well do without.

You, meanwhile, will no doubt find your voice making a noise in one of those tones which try to indicate that you are only taking a passive, almost academic interest really, but actually you are really inquiring with a view to establishing certain facts, like this bloke's everyday whereabouts so that you can pay some kneecap artist to pay him a visit on a dark night.

'Er . . . who was *that,* dear . . . ?' will be the extremely pathetic sound which will finally come out of your mouth.

'Oh *him,*' your partner will say in a tone which suggests at first that he had been so inconsequential as to not even rate her attention [though how could this possibly be the case as the pratt had been fawning over her all day, you begin to recall].

'Yes.. him' [you feel a sort of boldness coming into your voice . . . oh yes! . . . *YOU MEAN BUSINESS THIS TIME, AND NO* **MUCKING ABOUT***].*

'Oh . . . he's a **nobody** . . . but if you **must** know his name, he's Roddy Farquson Farquar' [or some other made up name like that – they **always** have made up names, these people]

Then she will add: ' It's a good job you were here to protect me – he's got such a **DREADFUL** reputation.'

'Such as?' you will find yourself saying, in a sort of knight-in-shining-white-armour [who nevertheless would like to bloody well know what Guinevere might get up to if he were not around], sort of voice.

At that she will shrug her shoulders in a sort of 'you won't trap me *that* easily buster' sort of way, and underline the unimportance of this man by busying herself with assorting the tack – which of course she will, after a few moments, turn to you to unravel.

You might think this incident finished, but then, as you are inevitably left to your own devices to pick and splutter through the tack unravelling procedure, you will hear some distance away the sound of school-girlish laughter.

As you stealthily peek around the corner of your horsebox, trying desperately to look as though you are devoting your entire attention to the tack you will be somewhat taken aback to see your partner, in the centre of a gaggle of other Know-it-All horsey types, with hand to her mouth as she giggles profusely.

You will then realise that the group is getting closer together as presumably more details are discussed, but you will still get the odd phrase which will ultimately take on an enigmatic turn of phrase when one of them, in a low voice, which is obviously much louder than intended, will bellow: ' . . . and I wouldn't think *you'd* be interested in someone like *him* anyway . . . after all, Jimmy keeps you *well satisfied* doesn't he? . . . '

In such a moment, as you try with ever increasing failure to get back to whatever you were doing when first abandoned, without your partner noticing in fact that you'd been eavesdropping on her private conversations, but realising that she *knows* that you were trying to listen in, *for Goodness sake DON'T* make matters any worse.

REPRESS that urge throbbing away in your chest to go in with hackles raised, wanting to know what on earth everyone is talking about – and certainly *NEVER EVEN THINK OF SUGGESTING* to your partner that she obviously discusses your own personal sex life with all of her Know-it-All horsey pals.

You should be aware from day one that she *does.* All the time. But she will never admit it. And if you're stupid enough to confront her with something mega-daft like: 'I hope you aren't discussing *our* sex life with your [Know-it-All] horsey friends . . .' you will get in return:

'HOW DARE YOU!!! . . . do you think for one moment that I would do a thing like THAT!!!! WHAT SORT OF A PERSON DO YOU TAKE ME FOR!!!!'

This will usually result in an attack of the sulks in the 'we'll have to resolve this one expensively' category.

However, you will *know* that she discusses *your* sex life in minute, painstaking, detail [as in every grunt and grind] because in general conversation with you she will, in unguarded moments, let out intimate details of the sex live of all her *other* Know-it-All-horsey pals, such as: 'You know Beth and Bernard haven't done it since last Thursday. He says he's got something on the end of his wotsit. She's very upset. I told her to take a lover . . . but of course she'd *never* do that . . . still . . . it must be *most* frustrating . . . I mean . . . five days . . . Trish suggested she borrow one of her aids . . . '

During these conversations, you will also gather that *all* of your partner's friends would, if given the right circumstances, abase themselves at the very feet of Rupert Farquson Farquson [or whatever his bloody name is] and simply *beg* him, if he were so disposed, and not doing anything else in particular, of course, such as picking his toes, to cart them off, in a spirit of pure academic interest to do with gaining further knowledge from his well documented encyclopaedic equestrian experience, you understand, **nothing more than that – understand!!** to a more comfortable place where they can discuss all matters to do with the equestrian world, such as bits, tack, saddles, events, fun rides, etc etc etc and also, while they're at it, and only if there is a bit of time left after all this in depth and informative and *totally necessary for their education* equestrian discussion . . . to . . . well . . . give them a damn good shag.

Though you *must* understand, such attitudes are confined purely to *all* of your partner's friends. There is **NEVER EVER** even the remotest suggestion that *she* holds similar desires. After all . . . hasn't she already told you that he's a nobody. . . what is more . . . he's a **SLIMY LITTLE CREEP** . . . an **OILY ITALIANATE GIT** . . . the sort who, were he not such a knowledgeable and experienced horse-mega-expert and **ABSOLUTELY WONDERFUL** rider. . . who is furthermore on the verge of the British Olympic Team and has a string of just dreamy wonderful stupendous, oh gosh I think I'm going to have an orgasm, horses, the like of whom make *even* dear old Dodo look like some sort of gutter snipe . . . she wouldn't even give him the time of day. . . because, after all . . . it's the *horses* which matter. . . and anyway. . . he's got such a **dreadful reputation** . . . and Carol said it is *so bad* that it seems to make him number one candidate for a modern revival of the Hell Fire Club . . . but he *does* seem to have an enormous cock . . . at least that's what Carol said . . . and after all, she's been to bed with him and they did it **FIFTEEN TIMES IN THE SAME NIGHT** . . . and God was he inventive. . . I'd never heard of that one position . . . but for **GOD'S SAKE** you'd better not ever divulge this fact to Barry... because that was told me in the **STRICTEST CONFIDENCE** . . . so it's more than your **LIFE'S WORTH** mate to even consider spilling the beans . . . and you'd better be careful with your tongue the next time you go down the pub with Barry. . . oh shit . . . I wish I'd never mentioned a word of this to you . . . **AND** you'd better not say a **WORD** to Tom about Trish's little indiscretion at the New Year bash . . . don't you remember, they seemed to be *gone* rather a long time . . . **NOR** come to think of it, Barbara's little *liaison* while Sam was working on the pipeline project in Dubai . . . it was **his fault** anyway for being away so long . . . and that **SHE** herself has **ABSOLUTELY NO INTEREST** in 'Rogering' Rupert whatsoever . . . **WHAT. . . INTERESTED IN HIM??????!!!!!** are you **BARMY OR SOMETHING!!!!** . . . I'm more interested in the rear end of a reticulated newt than I am in the front end of 'Big' Dick Farquar. . . oh yes . . . he's known as 'Dick' to those who know him well...not that *I* know him that well . . . it's just the name I've heard bandied about...second name's Richard. . . I suppose. . . can you help me unravel some more tack?

So, you see, you must **NEVER EVER SUGGEST THAT SHE HOLDS SIMILAR VIEWS** to all of the rest of her friends. 'It's quite *pathetic,* after all, that *grown women* should be taken in by such a slimy creep as *him.* I certainly see him for what he is . . . and I certainly found him to be nothing more than a big *turn off* when we had that in depth one-to-one discussion on dressage last November. . . you know. . . when you were in Scotland at that three day conference . . .'

BUYING THINGS

Buying things is an essential element of the horsey world. It is a sort of life blood of the whole thing. Without the ability to buy things on a regular basis – say 15 times a day on average – most horsey people would probably shoot themselves.

But of course, mention of that word 'ability' is where *you* often come in, because the moment they receive their *own* monthly pay cheque, family allowance, housekeeping, tax rebate, expenses etc etc, it is gleefully seized upon by the average horsey person and then swiftly blown on, well, buying things. Like that essential new bit for Dodo [his fourteenth since last month for God's sake!!], or his essential fifth rug this spring – the others being too small, too large, the wrong colour, the wrong smell [mummy's little boy just *can't* get on with it] etc etc.

For the rest of the month your services are required to provide the luxuries of life, such as food, electricity, heating in the winter, added of course to essential items, like buying more things for the horsey armoury.

The latter are often bought as part of a contractual agreement between you and your partner whereby you *loan* her the money because it is so desperately vital that she *must* have **TODAY!!!** this new Hackamore Jacket Potato Beef Dripping with Onions Botswanan Bridle – as recommended by [*WHO ELSE!!!*] Freddy Farquarson Farquarson – 'he said that by using it, I could achieve a much better rump position in the saddle and he's *such* a [dreamboat perhaps?] knowledgeable and expert horseman –Val does *everything* he tells her to do [*EVERYTHING???*] and look where it's got her. She's competing in the Intermediate Three Day Hunter Trial Dressage Races, and she's only been doing it for fifteen years!!! so I *must* *must* **MUST** have it, Jimmy *darling* and they only have one left, so I **MUST MUST MUST!!!!** have it – **AND** its only four hundred quid.'

Such a contract is, of course, struck under the strictest promise that, come next pay-day, you will **certainly** be repaid **in full** – after all, what's £400? A mere bagatelle.

Unfortunately for you, when that sainted day arrives, you are always just a tad too late. Before you have had the ability to splutter somewhat pathetically some sort of ridiculous suggestion that ' by the way...can you possibly...er...see your way to...er...possibly...er... repaying that £400 loan...er...s ort of thing...' you will quickly come to realise that the money has long been blown on another six Hackamore Jacket Potato Beef Dripping with Onions Botswanan Bridles – presumably so that she can have a steadily improving rump position in the saddle on each day of the week.

And it's no good reminding her at that point that she had suggested that there was only one of the damn things left in the entire universe which was why she so desperately needed the loan in the first place. The precise details of the conversation will not have been actually recalled, having slipped into the dim and distant past.

Nor is it any good dissolving into tears or paroxysms of rage. You are in the wonderful world of horses, remember, and in this wonderful world, things are bought and they are financed by walking chequebooks like you – so there is nothing more to do other than be a *MAN*, shrug the shoulders, write it up to experience and *PROMISE YOURSELF IN A SORT OF MAN-TO-MAN SORT OF WAY, WITH BRACED MUSCLES AND GIRDED LOINS AND A FOND REMINISCENCE OF HOW YOU DUFFED UP SOME SKINHEAD ONCE WHO WAS ANNOYING YOUR BIRD THAT YOU WILL:*

NEVER EVER LOAN HER MONEY AGAIN

Until, of course, five microseconds later when you hear the familiar dulcet tones of . . . 'Jimmy *darling* . . . Val tells me that . . .'

But before we go any further, let us take a more detailed look at some of the places, people and things which feature regularly in this aspect of the horsey world.

AT THE ꝏRSE SꝏP

Most horsey people will visit a **ꝏorse Shop** at least five times a day.

Your services will only be required when you are in walking chequebook mode, but this will still add up across a month, so it is important that you understand what this place is and how to survive it.

The first thing to understand is that **ꝏorse Shops** *never* have any thing in them that the customers actually want.

It might not seem that way, the first time you enter the hallowed portals of the main trading hall of such an establishment. After all, it looks like a veritable Aladdin's cave, packed from floor to ceiling with stuff – some of which you will actually recognise, like saddles and bits.

But what you must understand is that each and every one of the saddles is either too big or too small [as we have already discussed] the bits will not be *quite* what is required, the hundred of different chemical preparations for all the hundreds of different ailments won't work – at least they didn't when the little chap had that last bout of laminitis six weeks ago, but who cares, just to be on the safe side, we'll buy three times as much this time [but of course they never bloody well worked – for a start they are just combinations of salt, sugar and flour, and anyway they're not necessary because there was never anything wrong with him in the first place!!!] and the same philosophy will pervade for everything else that is sold in the Shop.

This, of course, is part of the terrific pleasure which horsey people derive from going there in the first place. It comes from the unspoken understanding – almost the first unwritten commandment of shopping in a horse shop, I suppose – that:

Buying Things

If what they actually want isn't there at that particular time
Then, it will definitely be in stock on the next visit, say, an hour later
[1 Equestrians, vv 21-22]

To which must be added the following supporting mantra:

But just in case what they actually want isn't in stock when they return
They'd better buy something that they certainly don't need *now*
[2 Gullabletwerps,vv 16-18]

And the same will hold for the next time. And the time after that. And so on and so forth ad infinitum, world without end, forever and forever, Amen.

Such a practice satisfies two basic needs:

1. *Expectation:* in the horse world, there is always something, somebody, and somewhere that is essentially better, larger, smoother, richer, longer, more successful etc than whatever is on offer at present. So there is always the constant need to strive for that new goal.

2. *The Compulsive Urge:* i.e. the needless and senseless spending of considerable amounts of money [which by now you should have noticed happens in the main to be *your* money].

So we can swiftly see, can we not, that the repeated visits to the Horse Shop offer a catharsis of almost mystical proportions in the life of the horsey person. And of course that realisation leads us to the understanding that the Horse Shop, at least as far as the horsey people are concerned, is in reality a Temple.

It is important that you understand that fact, because it will help you survive, and it will also help you to recognise those tell-tale signs as you enter the Horse Shop's magical and mystical inner enclave.

Look for the careful way in which your partner opens the door, as though approaching a devotional, and the sudden descent into hushed tones.

Recognise the bowed and stooped stance – had she a veil, she would surely be putting it on at this moment – and the reverent manner in which she addresses the Horse Shop woman, who, for all intents and purposes should be looked upon as some sort of High Priestess of the Holy Horsey Horder, with the first responses:

'Is my New Zealand Rug Ready?'

I suspect that this sort of question is rather like a kind of code which to the horsey people translates into something like:

Buying Things

'Forgive me, Mother, for I have sinned
I have erred and strayed from the divine pathway
In that the other day for one nanosecond I
Had unhorsey thoughts
And there is no health in me...'

Similarly, there is an obvious coded reply in the response which the horse shop woman gives:

'I'll look in the book'

I say this because this always sparks off a very formalised, if not ritualistic, activity between all involved, rather like the first reading at a Church Service.

Your partner will immediately take a seat. An acolyte from the Horse Shop, dressed in ceremonial gear of boots, jods, a body warmer and a thick jumper – even in the height of Summer – will emerge from somewhere at the back of the shop carrying a large tome, which she will hand to the High Priestess – sorry, Horse Shop woman.

She will then turn towards your partner and start thumbing through the pages of the book while humming to herself – or, you wonder, is she *really* incanting some mystical magical chant which should always accompany the opening of the sacred tome?

Then she will reach a page and take a mystical and very significant deep intake of breath, look heavenwards for a magical moment, her eyes rolling towards the sky, then gaze full face at your partner. The reverential responses will then re-commence at that moment:

98

Buying Things

'Mrs Squib'

'Yes'

'It's not in yet'

'Oh.   When?'

'Definitely the next time you come in'

'What happened? I thought it would be in by today'

'Yes.   The order came in, but there was a cock up and we
sold your's to somebody else.   Sorry'

'Do you have any others?'

'Yes.   There are many, but they are all the wrong size'

'Can I have one of those to tide me over'

'Yes.   Of course'

'In that case I'll take five'

'Can I interest you in something else'

'Of course.   Anything.'

'How about this?'

'What is it?'

'A clockwork model of Roddy Farquason Farquar.
You just wind him up and he does something
Disgusting with his right hand.
It's very useless'

'How much?'

'Seven hundred pounds'

'I'll take two – er … Jimmy darling

[Here endeth the umpteenth lesson]

99

BUYING THE TRAILER

On first sight, you probably thought that the horse and rider made some sort of a joint combination.

Your partner sat on the horse, and the horse took her wherever she wanted to go. Sounded logical, didn't it?

Now, of course, you know much better. The horse itself *requires transport of its own.* To take him from wherever he's kept to wherever your partner wants to ride him, and back again.

It's rather like having a car of your own, but instead of taking it out for a spin from your own home, you load it onto a car transporter which is so large and cumbersome as to be impossible traffic even on the M6 – but then taking it down some forgotten single lane trackway deep in the middle of nowhere, so that you can get the car out and take it for a spin of, say, a couple of miles or so – and then putting the car back into the transporter so that you can go over all that forgotten trackway stuff again until you finally get back to where you started in the first place.

Logical eh?

Anyway, you know only too well by now not to apply any reason or logic to any situation in the horsey world, so just accept it as a fact.

The first such conveyance which your partner will desperately need **TODAY!!!** will be a *trailer.*

This is a sort of portable stable on wheels which carries with it the added advantages, for your partner and any other horsey person for that matter, that very shortly after its first journey, the horse will deposit vast amounts of muck inside it – so muck-frollicking will be on the menu *wherever your partner happens to be.*

If you were seriously into muckfrollicking, you will instantly recognise what a tremendous facility a horse trailer thus provides – rather like having a portable 12 screen surround sound cinema complex on wheels for the rest of us.

The other important fact to bear in mind is that [and by now you should anticipate what I'm going to say – if not, then you've hardly been paying any attention] the moment this vitally important 'I've just got to have it' horse trailer arrives in your possession, it will be **totally useless and completely unacceptable** and of course **will have to be replaced** by something much bigger, better, more luxurious and of course **much more expensive.**

The first inkling of the arrival into your life of this muckheap on wheels will come one evening as you are relaxing, and enjoying the soothing effects of your second bottle of scotch since tea time.

Across a darkened room, in the dim distance beyond the deception of an otherwise reassuring comfort of lamp light glow, a voice will emerge from the rustle of a newspaper:

'Jimmy... there's a trailer advertised here. What do you think...?'

It might seem reasonable for you to answer that you don't know what on earth your partner is talking about, but as we have already seen, this is strictly inadvisable. simply say something void like: 'Oh?'

If you get away with it, the matter will be terminated and your partner will return to the paper. More likely than not, however, the matter will not rest there and you will hear something which clearly demonstrates that her vague annoyance like: 'No... listen... this is important... it's a... Fungle Trumpet Two Compartment Long Wheelbase 1953... so what do you think?'

At this point, be **extremely** careful. You must on **no account** demonstrate your ignorance by saying something like: 'I don't know anything about what you are talking about'. **Nor** must you sound sarcastic by saying something like: 'Sounds like a **real bargain** to me – no doubt Ferdie Farquson Farquar – or whatever his name is – would agree, and or course, good old Adrian...'

Neither of these approaches are to be attempted. Instead, take a middle course by sounding supportive and helpful.

Say something like: Hmmm... I think I've *heard* of one of those... aren't they supposed to be **pretty good?**'

Such an approach will protect you from negativity, and might even bring you some encouraging comments.

If this is the case, you could even push your luck a little more by following up with: ' How much do they want?'

Show no emotion when the voice from behind the paper says something like: "Five grand", and **resist at all costs** imploding into: '**WHAT????!!! YOU'RE THINKING OF SPENDING FIVE THOUSAND QUID FOR A BEATEN UP OLD HEAP OF JUNK ONLY HALF ON WHEELS WHICH IS MOREOVER MORE THAN FORTY YEARS OLD!!!! YOU MUST BE BARMY...**'

Yes, you've probably recognised already the two crass errors here:

1. *She* won't be spending the money. **You will.**

2. It is rather pointless stating the obvious. As we have already established, your partner *is* barmy, so her intended course of action is perfectly logical.

What you must do is stay calm, and say something like: 'Well, I suppose it's worth inspecting . . . perhaps with a more expert opinion.'

That's a clever sort of answer, because, as we have already discussed *no one* knows more about horses than your partner, and therefore *no one* knows more about trailers.

So you will find yourself the next day in some far away distant horse yard, as the rain drizzles around your ears, inspecting the peeling paintwork, rusting rivets and fading bodywork as you wander around rotting pieces of timber loosely attached to a rapidly deteriorating metal chassis and thinking to yourself: '*This,* then, is a Fungle Trumpet Two Compartment Long Wheelbase 1953 . . . Oh Lord!!!'

Your partner will be in generally horsey negotiating mode: pretending to be completely indifferent [even at times, downright rude] to whatever is the sales pitch, while underneath, and, to be frank, not concealing it all that well, being ecstatic at the incredible bargain which she – sorry *you* – are inevitably about to purchase.

The vendor will be another know-it-all horsey type so in addition to the indifference/ecstatic nature of the conversation, there will be a continuing contest between the two of them aimed at demonstrating once and for all that one knows *everything* there is to know about horses and of course the other knows *sod all.*

You, meanwhile, will be stuck somewhere in the middle umming and ahhing as each body blow is delivered between the two combatants. But for goodness sake **let them get on with it –** **DON'T, WHATEVER YOU DO, JOIN IN.**

The conversation will go something like this:

[Your partner] 'Seems a bit old to me'

[The other know-it-all horsey type] 'Yes . . . but it's a Fungle Trumpet Two Compartment Long Wheelbase 1953 – *everyone* knows that *they* go on for ever.'

[Your partner] 'Quite, but this seems to have had some rough treatment.'

[The other know-it-all horsey type] ' No more than would usually be associated with a top equestrian expert like *me.* By the way, I didn't see *you* at the Upton Snodsbury In Hand Big Hands Hasn't Roddy Farquson Farquer Got *Gorgeous* Sensitive Understanding Yet So *MASCULINE* And *DOMINATING* Hands Dressage Jumping Olympic Qualifier the other week . . . I'm sure you're just *dying* to know where *I* came . . . well, I came *FIRST* actually.'

[Your partner] 'No. I was at the Ashton Manor Class One Three Day Hunter Trial Qualifier for the Entire Universe Championship on one of Billy Baffin Land's stallions . . . those wheels look a bit wobbly . . .'

[The other know-it-all horsey type] 'Normal wear and tear . . . look, do you want this trailer or not, fat arse.'

[Your partner] 'I'm still thinking about it . . . you look the sort of big nosed moron that *Tony* would refuse to deal with at any price – by the way, who *is* your Farrier . . . ?'

[The other know-it-all and by now distinctly wobbly looking horsey type] 'Er . . . [WE'VE GOT HER ON THE RUN...WE'VE GOT HER ON THE RUN . . . EE, AY, ADIO, WE'VE GOT HER ON THE RUN] I . . . er . . . do my own shoeing, actually'

[Your triumphant partner] Precisely. Well it's not really what I'm looking for . . . and anyway you are not only the sort of moron who has to do her own shoeing, but I'd bet you've never had a one-to-one expert training session with Rupert Farquar Farquarson. [oops, bit of a gooley been dropped I think]

[The other know-it-all and rallying horsey type] Well I've got two thousand other people who are simply queuing up to buy it, so you'd better make up your mind quickly . . . and by the way *Rupey* took me through my Hunter Trials Dressage paces only last week while Alan was rock climbing in East Anglia, and not only did he improve my overall rump position with his *amazing* wealth of experience but he also gave me a good stiff rogering as well. Lasted for *five solid hours.* I don't know who was more shagged out afterwards – Alan with his rock climbing or me with my pole-vaulting.

[Your by now curiously *defensive* partner] Well . . . it might suit my purposes for a couple of days . . . how much did you say it was . . . five quid? [and **FOR GOD'S SAKE PLEASE** no more mention of Rupert Farquarson Farquar while Jimmy's here]

[The other know-it-all [OK I won't say another word, but let this be a lesson to you]horsey type] 'Five *thousand* actually.'

[Here beginneth the sacred ritual of horse trading. The parameters have now been established, the insults been hurled. These two now know where each other is coming from and you *know* you're in for some rough, tough bargaining.]

[Your partner, obviously in a rough, tough, no-nonsense negotiating mood] 'Oh. All right. I'll offer you six thousand and not a penny less.'

[The other know-it-all horsey type] 'Done'

At this point, the two will shake hands and treat each other as bosom pals going back over the last four centuries. Your partner will then accept the inevitable invitation to 'look over the yard' and will disappear with the vendor in intense conversation which, every now and then will throw up little lines that you might recognise, such as: ' . . . oh you *know* Adrian do you . . .' and ' . . . yes, I *know* Freddy Farquarson Farquarson has such a *dreadful* reputation, but you *know* what it's like when he shows you his technique . . .' leaving you to look over your wonderful new purchase.

It may strike you at this time that you may have been somewhat naive in the thought that bargaining from a horse trading point of view – as you *understood* it to be, that is – usually involved the *purchaser* beating the *vendor **down*** in price rather than settling for an amount **considerably above** the original asking price.

Such misgivings will, of course, be instantly dispelled as the tearful farewells having been made [your *partner* with the vendor, the *vendor* with the Fungle Trumpet Two Compartment Long Wheelbase 1953, you with your cash] and you begin the rickety rackety journey across the uncompromising potholes of the vendor's drive way.

You may venture: 'but I thought the asking price was only five thousand – so how come we paid *six?*'

But then of course will come the reassurance: 'Yes, but we're talking about a Fungle Trumpet Two Compartment Long Wheelbase 1953. *Anyone* who knows *anything* about horses *knows* that they don't come for a penny piece under six thousand. That woman didn't know the *first thing* about horses. Believe me, we've got the ***BARGAIN OF THE CENTURY!!!*** And she was asking a miserly ***FIVE THOUSAND*** . . . she me be totally and absolutely round the twist. You wait till I tell Val, and Di and Adrian and Cath and . . .'

At that moment, a loud noise behind you will signify that you have driven over that sarsen standing stone of a boulder in the middle of the trackway perhaps a little too swiftly, and the side of the aforementioned Fungle Trumpet Two Compartment Long Wheelbase 1953 has just fallen off.

DODO MEETS THE TRAILER

The process of buying the second trailer will begin the moment that the Fungle Trumpet Two Compartment Long Wheelbase 1953 makes its triumphal entry into your field.

As you struggle with the lock on the field gate, and then eventually make progress across the deep rutted field entrance, resulting in even more bits and pieces falling off the Fungle Trumpet Two Compartment Long Wheelbase 1953, you will become aware, out of the corner of your eye, that you are under intense scrutiny.

And it will become plainly obvious in the short space of time that it takes your head to turn towards the object making its relentless way towards you that Dodo is decidedly not amused.

This will be confirmed by the way he will confront the Fungle Trumpet Two Compartment Long Wheelbase 1953 – in a sort of 'head on' sort of way. Then the various cow kicks he will put into the body work, one of which will drive a natty little hole through the side which was left remaining after your original encounter with the sarsen standing stone – at which point you will notice that the natty little hole seems to be getting wider by the moment – dry rot has obviously set in.

Dodo will then snort, put in a few bucks and gallop off into the far distance, as though planning on never being seen again.

You will then become aware of a rather concerned presence standing next to you.

'He doesn't seem too keen,' she will say.

'No,' you will say, resisting the temptation to say something daftly obvious like: 'You don't say. **REALLY????** I would *never* have guessed it. A blind beggar could have told me that.'

Then you will say something reassuring [if you have learned anything that is] like: 'It's all *new* to him. I'm sure he will get used to it.' [and then feel that old chest of yours fill out in a manly 'I'm the man around here and one of my lifelong tasks is to make everything perfect, everything right – thank *God* for us masterful men and so to *HELL with Burgundy*' sort of way].

But of course Dodo *won't* get used to it. Having the Fungle Trumpet Two Compartment Long Wheelbase 1953 on board means going out and actually being ridden, and that sort of situation has got to be resisted at all costs.

So every occasion when the Fungle Trumpet Two Compartment Long Wheelbase 1953 is brought out in a state where it looks as though it is about to be used, battle stations will prevail.

If you have any sense, *never* be present during such events. Volunteer for overseas secondment. Join the Navy. Get yourself wrongly accused of armed robbery. Do *anything* but be in that field. To do otherwise will inevitably land you with severe injuries and no amount of negatives clocking up on the old tally.

As a means of demonstrating what I'm saying – and also to act as a tidy warning to any of you who might be beguiled into going along, let us, for a moment, assume that you *are* stupid enough to be there. This is what you must avoid.

First of all, as your partner arrives, Dodo will disappear from sight. Over the brow of the hill, with a snort and a shake of his head.

If *you* are there, you will be summarily dispatched with head collar to get him back, on the basis that your partner needs to attend to the Fungal Trumpet Two Compartment Long Wheelbase 1953.

To help you along the way, you will be given a handful of biscuits, or mints or some other sort of tit bit that Dodo supposedly likes.

You will then tramp through mud up to your armpits, fighting through couch grass wrapping itself around your heels, and doing everything to ensure that you are definitely in with a chance in the next Dr Livingstone look-alike contest, before you round some rocks and are confronted with the snorting and hateful features of Dodo.

You will know, if you didn't know already, that you are in for trouble by the tell-tale way in which he is pounding the ground, and the stones underneath are being systematically ground to dust.

At such a time, it is worth remembering that you are a **MAN,** that you are not going to let any **damned beast of burden** push you around: **SO BE BOLD AND RESOLUTE: GO FORWARD, MY BRAVE MAN WITH FORTITUDE AND COURAGE AND SO TO HELL WITH BURGUNDY** etc etc etc – [oh not *that* matinee idol routine again – get a life, before it's too late, saddo].

Then, when Dodo has given you a good kick in the goolies, try not to be so pathetic as you writhe around clutching what is left of your manhood, and comfort yourself with the feeling that you have been successful, because, as you try to pick yourself up and stagger forwards, feeling that your balls have almost certainly dropped past your kneecaps, you will be rewarded with the sight of Dodo, docile as ever, trotting majestically down the hill towards your partner.

By the time you reach them – it might take you several hours, by the way – Dodo will have been comforted, cosseted and be standing in his rug, which unfortunately is a little on the small size, but that was all the horse shop had in at the time, and he will look back towards you with a sneer on his face as if he's saying: 'Stitch that one, then, Jimmy. Finding it a bit difficult to *walk* are we pal?'

Remember, as you try to reach for the nearest boulder to smash into his teeth that your partner is present, no doubt chastising you for not getting him in his head collar in the first place – 'Thank goodness I bought sixteen head collars when I was in the horse shop a couple of hours ago, and I had a spare – even though it's not *quite* the right size, but it will do. But it's no thanks to *you*. I only asked you to go and catch him, for goodness sake. It's not as though it's difficult is it? It's nowhere near as difficult as what we've got to do now. . .'

At that you will be handed some tangled up tack to unravel, but you won't have any extended amount of time to carry out this little exercise this time, because your partner will have moved to the back of the Fungle Trumpet Two Compartment Long Wheelbase 1953 and will be fiddling with the catch on the back ramp.

You will know you've become involved when she says: 'Give us a hand with this will you.'

Leaving your tack unravelling duties for a second, you will address yourself to the best possible way of coming out of this one with most of your fingers intact, as you pick at the corroded catch, which will be of a type which only ever seems to be used in the horsey world.

It comprises a bracket with an 'O' ring into which is located a shaft with a hinged tongue at the end, which is supposed to fold down neatly when the assembly is secured, thus preventing it from coming apart. Such an arrangement lasts about a day after the new catch has left the manufacturer. For the rest of its life, it's in a well corroded state, jamming at every opportunity and developing a sort of in-built booby trap arrangement.

So that, as you pick and pull at it, the catch will suddenly spring open, and the trailer ramp rapidly descent on *your* head – causing your partner to dissolve into peels of uncontrollable laughter watching you frolicking about, with one hand attending to your bruised cranium and the other still soothing your troubled groin. Gosh, you *do* look a hilarious sight, it has to be said. I can't understand why *you* don't seem to see the funny side of it.

Next on the agenda is, of course, putting Dodo *inside* the trailer.

He will, of course, resolutely refuse to do this. Half a tonne of biscuits and mints later, he will still be resolutely refusing. Half an hour of hoarse voices cajoling, shouting, cursing, after that and he will *still* be resolutely refusing.

Fourteen hours later, as darkness begins to cloak you [and it is here that you may recall that this exercise in paranoia started at 6am] he will still be resolutely refusing.

Your partner will be close to tears as she slumps into a heap, head in hands as she wails: 'It's no use . . . *no use* . . . Jimmy . . . what on earth are we *going to do*?'

It might still seem to you that a simple solution would end this purgatory and you might feel tempted to answer: 'Shoot him, for pity's sake and let's be done with it. Then the two of us can go off together into the sunset to a new beginning, to a new life together, striding towards a new era, and so to hell with....'

But I would trust that you know by now that this is not the sort of thing to say at a moment like this.

Anyway, the moment will almost certainly resolve itself, because when Dodo has realised that he has finally won, and that he has extracted every last ounce of satisfaction, pain, pleasure and abject terror [that one is reserved specifically for you, by the way] out of the situation, he will walk, unaided, and as docile as a lamb into the Fungle Trumpet Two Compartment Long Wheelbase 1953 and begin to gorge himself on the hay net inside.

At such a moment, you might hear the vague ticking of something inside. Your partner will go to investigate and then utter something like: ' Oh of course...of course... Jimmy, why on earth didn't you think of it...after all you're supposed to be the one with the brains round here...'

You might say something like: ' Think of what?'

"The Clockwork model of Freddy Farquar Farquarson. You know little Dodo boy just *loves* his little *Freddy*... especially when Freddy does that peculiar action with his right hand... come to think of it, you were going to tell me what he's supposed to be doing...'

Notwithstanding the intervention of a mechanical pervert, such events as these will be the norm, and you will know that the days of the Fungle Trumpet Two Compartment Long Wheelbase 1953 are numbered when the conversation seems to have more than the usual edge of anxt.

Phrases such as: 'I'm sure he's not happy with it...' will pepper the breakfast cereal, and then, you'll know things are definitely afoot when you hear: 'Barry's just bought Val a Twistleton-Smyth Four Wheel Front Loader 1961.

As if there was not enough incentive for change anyway, this is the final straw – a close horsey chum with something easily perceived as better, stronger, bigger etc etc etc...

It will be rather like deja vu all over again, again, as you sit one evening relaxing and enjoying the soothing effects of your second bottle of scotch since tea time.

Across a darkened room, in the dim distance between the deception of an otherwise reassuring comfort of lamp light glow, a voice will emerge from the rustle of a newspaper:

'Jimmy... there's a trailer advertised here. A Twistleton-Smyth Four Wheel Front Loader 1962. What do you think...?'

BUYING THE LORRY

Sometime after the purchase of the forty third trailer [a Clive 'Big' Pratt Ultimate Muckfrollicker on Wheels Long Wheelbase Front, Back, Side, Top and Bottom Loading 16 Wheel with 90 Speaker Sound System Glamrock Bell Bottom Trousers and Embarrassing Hairdo1978 – you *always* end up with one of those], you will hear an ominous, but all too familiar dirge: 'Val's got a lorry. She traded her Clive 'Big' Pratt Ultimate Muckfrollicker on Wheels Long Wheelbase Front, Back, Side, Top and Bottom Loading 16 Wheel with 90 Speaker Sound System Glamrock Bell Bottom Trousers and Embarrassing Hairdo1978 for it. '

RESIST all temptations to be flippant. She said **LORRY**, not **LOLLY** and you *know* you heard her correctly, so don't start making wise cracks about: 'I thought she was a little too old for that sort of children's confectionery at her age . . . 'etc

NOR must you make sarcastic and disparaging remarks along the lines of: 'I was only thinking the other day that it was about time Val got off her fat arse and started doing a proper day's work – and come to think of it, lorry driving will suit her' and all that sort of thing.

You *know* what your partner is on about, and by this time, even though you've got through the turnover of a multi national corporation in your trailer buying activities, you *know* that it's only a matter of time before *you* hear the tiny patter of tyres coming up *your* drive. So **GIVE IN GRACEFULLY.**

You *like* your regular visits to the Bank Manager, after all – and he *likes* seeing you. He even gets the tea and biscuits out every time you come to arrange the new finance packages these day, so it's not such a bad life at all, is it?

However, one word of warning – and especially for those of you who have not yet reached *this* particular stage.

You buy trailers from other know-it-all horsey people in the main. Lorries, on the other hand *can* be bought from other know-it-all horsey people, but, like old bangers, they are more often than not bought from **Dealers.**

Wherein lies my warning.

It is a matter of historical fact that the average car salesman was the natural successor to the old horse dealer. As horses were used less and less for day to day transport, and people took to motor vehicles, so the majority of horse dealers [who, it will be remembered by all you history anoraks out there, contain within their ranks a group of people descended from what was left of the warring Iceni tribe after the Romans had marmalised them, hence their constant desire throughout history to shaft the establishment and rob them of all their money. I should **strongly point** out here that these should not be confused with the **vast majority of fine,** *professional, law abiding and upstanding dealers who would certainly NEVER EVER sell a 92 year old clapped out gelding as a 2 year old stallion and who I feel should be given Olympic Medals for their honesty]* Anyway – where were we? Oh yes, the horse dealers on account of changing times switched to the new technology and brought their natural abilities for ~~cheating, lying, conning, double-dealing, dressing up mutton to look like lamb etc etc~~ honesty, integrity, decency, straightforwardness and professional expertise to a new age.

A few, however, remained loyal to the old ways and continued in the horse trade [more of these anon] while some of the remaining group decided to bridge the gap between old and new, and become **Horse Lorry Dealers** most of which, of course, are **MOST CERTAINLY ALSO GLOWING EXAMPLES OF FINE LAW ABIDING CITIZENS WHO DESERVE EVERY ACCOLADE THAT CAN BE HEAPED UPON THEM.** Unfortunately, as with the horse dealers, there are a few – the real reptilian ones – who let the side down, and you know that with your luck you are just *bound* to run into one of these.

You will know, once the evening conversation with the talking newspaper has taken place and you find yourself *yet again* far away in some forgotten and forsaken land looking at the latest piece of junk to be paraded as the finest bargain since Edward the Confessor flogged England at a knock down price to William the Conqueror – that you are up against one of *this* type [i.e. *totally unrepresentative of the vast majority of fine upstanding guys*] of Horse Lorry Dealer very quickly into the conversation.

Unlike the know-it-all horsey people you've been dealing with over the past weeks and months in the quest for your 43 lorries, ending up with your prized Clive 'Big' Pratt Ultimate Muckfrollicker on Wheels Long Wheelbase Front, Back, Side, Top and Bottom Loading 16 Wheel with 90 Speaker Sound System Glamrock Bell Bottom Trousers and Embarrassing Hairdo1978, this git will know as much as you seem to do about lorries.

You, unlike most of the know-it-all horsey people, including your partner, know that the funny lumps of metal under the flap at the front of the lorry constitute something called an 'Engine', and it is this 'Engine' which, under certain conditions too complicated and unimportant to go into now, makes the 'Wheels' go around, thus permitting the lorry to move forward.

You can establish just how much the Reptilian Horse Lorry Dealer really knows very quickly by asking a probing, knock-out sort of question such as: 'What size is the 'engine''

If this bloke, rather than looking blankly at you in a way which suggests that the question formulating itself in *his* mind is: 'What's an 'engine'?', stares back at you and impassively says: '2.3 litre diesel', you will know straightaway that you are on extremely dangerous territory. You have entered the reptile's lair – or whatever reptiles live in.

Your partner will be quite oblivious, of course. *She* will be busying herself with the logistics of where the bigger piles of muck will fall on the interior accommodation, where the air conditioning system for Dodo to enjoy in the summer is placed, where Dodo's cocktail bar is going to be positioned, and where the wardrobe for his smoking jackets is located.

The hard talking, on this occasion, will be left to *you* – after all, you *are* supposed to be a man, aren't you, and aren't *all* men supposed to know *everything* there is to know about motors and all that sort of thing?

You will try. Maybe, you will try pointing out that this lorry looks familiar – like something they used in the old cinema newsreels taken at Tobruck during World War II.

You might also attempt comments aimed at establishing whether this lorry is subject to something called 'Italian Engineering', and hadn't you noticed in your cursory examination of that self-same 'Italian Engineering' something which looked suspiciously like a left handed thread on the bi-valve relay?

It will all be to no avail. You are up against formidable forces here – a bloke with knowledge both of engines *and* horses and what's more, a professional vehicle dealer to boot.

You will know you are lost when the patter starts to include your partner.

She, having made her mind up already that this is **exactly what she wants** – yes, I know that's what she said of all the other fifty or so lorries you've seen today, but **this one** is **definitely the one.** And what's more it must **definitely** be purchased **TODAY!!!** After all, it's the Burwash Carbonell In Hand 16.2 Upside Down Back to Front Left Diagonal Going Right competition tomorrow, and wouldn't Val be just that incey wincey bit **peeved** if Dodo were to arrive majestically in **this?** You will know finally that all is lost when she emerges from her tour of inspection with that tell-tale and fatal look of enthusiasm on her face.

At that, the Horse Lorry Dealer bloke will go for the jugular.

'Tasty piece of kit, eh love?' [yes, I *know* that's all very condescending and sexist, and I *know* that under strict P.C. guidelines I should by now be issuing world wide statements that I unequivocally want everyone to understand that I believe women are not just sex objects who are put on this planet for the titillation of male chauvinist pigs but are fully capable and equal members of society and what is more much much *better and EVEN MORE CAPABLE* than the majority of weedy wimpish blokes who are only on the planet to provide the odd dose of baby making fluid – as well as paying for everything of course – that is, until science finally makes men totally redundant. But *this* Horse Lorry Dealer bloke doesn't care a monkey's about any of that hedonist crap. All he's interested in is shifting heaps of scrap for huge sums of money to any naive Sheila who's gone so barmy about horses that she'd believe anything he tells her – so it's all rather irrelevant].

Your partner won't answer. She'll have fully entered the euphoric world of dreams, pinning rosettes onto Dodo and taking laps of honour and watching Val's tortured expressions of envy as she drives *ever so slowly* past her in a sort of *Royal Progress* sort of way.

But then, the Horse Lorry Dealer bloke will evoke his master stroke. Adjusting his Robin Hood hat and scratching his pencil thin moustache in a sort of knowing way, he will turn to her with a distinct undertone of 'promise me you won't breath a word of what I'm going to tell you to anyone, and when you've told all your know-it-all horsey pals similarly swear them to the strictest secrecy' to his voice, he will say: ' I...er...believe it once belonged to Freddy Farquar Farquarson – or so I'm led to believe...'

That's it. Argument over. There is even no point in trying to attempt to shave even just a few pence off the £200,000 asking price. Nor in enquiring why, since the moment you arrived on the scene, the Horse Lorry Dealer bloke had resolutely stood in front of the back axle, concealing it from your view at all times, and even, with a deft half nelson or two, bodily removed you from that area whenever you tried to get a closer look.

Just ensure that you stop at some convenient off-licence on the way home. You will need some extra companionship, because the ritual calls *this* time will last far into the night.

Which brings me on to the next section of this little guide:

BUYING THE SECOND LORRY

or it would have done, but I think you've had enough by now, so we will turn to the next subject which I have deliberately held over until now because I am afraid to say, it is of such a diabolical nature as to be the stuff of things far beyond your wildest and most dreadful nightmares, the stuff of terrors from beneath the very caverns of primeval earth which sometimes manifest themselves by spewing up in very expensive special effects in Hollywood movies to the accompaniment of all those meaningless Medieval chants – and always as the tempest seems to be at its height, all those crash bang wallops and lightning bolts and instantly dying flowers and baying wolves that seem to have strayed onto the set from the local zoo etc etc.

But first: I think we should just take a moment's pause before we go any further so that I can ask you a very important question.

Have you consulted your Doctor lately?

If not, then I would be extremely derelict in my duty if I were not to advise you to do so now with a strong recommendation that he puts you onto a course of zombie pills before turning this page.

For now we are going to explore the matter of

BUYING A SECOND HORSE

It will follow as surely as night follows day that having just *one* horse is *never* enough.

True, only *one* horse can be ridden at any *one* time, but remember that, as we have already discussed, the actual business of *riding* the damn thing is only a very minor consideration, and hardly ever takes place anyway.

The *real* raison d'être is the ability to spend oodles and oodles of dosh, so what better way of achieving this goal than to **double it all up?**

Two nags means *two* lots of everything [yes, *even* clockwork Freddy Farquar Farquarsons!!] – so instead of 16 New Zealand rugs of the wrong size per week, you can have 32 New Zealand rugs of the wrong size. And just think of all the bits that you can have!!!!

Some of you who are still so naive that I am really beginning to wonder whether you've bothered to take in a single word of this guide might suggest something to yourself which is in the Premier Division Imbecile Class along the lines of: 'Why don't the two horses *share* everything, then I won't have to buy double the quantities?'

Yes. I can hear the rest of you convulsing into side splitting laughter right now, and perhaps thinking that the term 'Loppy Lugs' might be appropriately applied, but enough of this. For the benefit of the mega morons still out there perhaps I should explain.

First of all, Dodo doesn't *share* anything, and secondly, such a stupid suggestion of cost cutting could only come from people who know *nothing* about the horsey world – like Bank Managers, for instance.

Such people just do not *understand* the whole ethic of the horsey world, nor do they take in the fact that Dodo at some stage in his life will

(a) need a companion

and

(b) need replacing.

The second point here is rather crucial. You probably thought that Dodo, like every other living thing on the planet will one day hop his clogs [sorry, hop his extremely expensive extra therapeutic shoes].

Well, *yes*, he will – though you will probably have to wait **30 to 40 years** I'm afraid for this wonderful day to arrive.

BUT DON'T under any circumstances allow yourself to believe that this will be the end of matters. To do so would be an ***extremely dangerous delusion.***

Sometime after Dodo's 12th birthday, as you are taking down the balloons and bunting from the stable and the 'HAPPY BIRTHDAY MUMMY'S *FAVOURITE* INCEY WINCEY LITTLE SQUIRREL NUTKIN' posters from the lamp posts in the village, there will be the first hint of what is to come.

You will be humming a sort of 'Onward Christian Soldiers' sort of stiff-upper-lip-come-on-lad-you-*know*-life's-crap-but-it-could-be-crapper-just-think-of-the-starving-millions-so-make-the-most-of-standing-here-like-a-stuffed-herbert-prompting-delerious-derision-from-all-and-sundry-as-you-take-down-these-ridiculous-posters-even-though-you-*really*-wish-you-were-down-the-pub-right-now-or-perhaps-sticking-your-head-forcibly-in-a-bucket-of-meths sort of tune, when your ears will pick up the gist of a conversation on your partner's mobile phone, which she bought [sorry, which *you* bought for her] specifically so that she could make any number of ritual **premium rate** calls from anywhere, even in the saddle.

The odd word will waft your way: ' . . . oh . . . you haven't have you? . . . you *haven't* . . . what? . . . *a five year old???* . . . . *16.3?????* . . . what's his name?? . . . Ashington Abbots Rural Development Grant Aid III??? . . . that's a nice name . . . I wonder where that name came from . . . yes . . . oh I see . . . but what's his other . . . name . . . oh Scumbag eh? . . . that's a **great** name . . . '

The conversation will drift away from you again and those of you to whom the term 'loppy lugs' *even now* **still** applies will think that this is some sort of typically innocuous diatribe.

Any such feelings will be immediately dispelled at the end of the call, however.

You will be confronted by your partner looking like thunder, at which point the tune you are humming will undoubtedly change from 'Onward Christian Soldiers' to something more akin to 'Nearer My God to Thee . . .'

Rest easy. On this occasion, you are not the cause of your partner's ire.

'Jimmy... have a guess what Di has just gone and done... God I could **KILL** her...'

RESIST saying something like: 'If you'd have killed Di, then she would have Di-ed, ha, ha, ha...' This will only serve to damage the, so far, trouble free position you are enjoying and might also lead to a rather unpleasant stabbing pain in the region of your groin.

You must say something like: 'Oh, what's she gone and done now?' you may feel like putting a slight sneering tone on that final *'now'* as though you're implying that Di does lots and lots of stupid things all the time.

This might go in your favour at this particular juncture, though of course I would counsel you to be extremely selective in your use of this technique as you might accidentally put the sneering *'now'* in at a time when Di is very much flavour of the month. In which case you'll be in extremely dangerous territory signalled by the foreboding: 'Di's OK. She *means well* and she's leant me her Kimberwick Fish & Chips Ultra Curry Sauce with Saveloy and Mushy Peas Four Day Dressage Bit for a few days to see if Dodo gets on with it before I buy 30 of them – by the way I'm thinking of renaming the house after her...'

Anyway, back to the action. Remember, you were achieving a certain amount of kudos by the strategic use of the sneering 'What's she gone and done *now?'*

'Only gone and bought another horse!!!... I mean... HER!!!... gone and bought another horse... an Irish Draft Cross Thoroughbred 16.3 Bay Gelding [**DON'T TRY** to fathom out what this means, just accept that this gobbledegook means that it's a type of horse – but you knew that already, so don't bother to ask any more questions]... a 16.3!!!... at **HER AGE!!!**... and it's only **FIVE YEARS OLD!!!!**... God, she's going to have trouble... I'd *never* have believed it... and after all, what does *she* know about horses... bugger all... she doesn't know the *first thing*... so what on earth she's doing having **TWO**... don't get me wrong...she *means well*... and **I'M DEFINITELY NOT PEEVED... DEFINITELY NOT**... how could anyone think that?????... it's just that I thought Squidgey was *everything* to her... and now she's gone and got this other one... paid just £45,000 for it... I mean £45,000!!!!!!!!... I've never heard of **SUCH AN INCREDIBLE BARGAIN**... you know what she's going to call it?....' [but I don't think I really need to add too much more at this point, as I'm sure you've got the picture, and even any loppy lugs out there must surely know what's coming next]

By now, you should have heard enough to raise those all too familiar alarms in your mind. Something, you know, is afoot.

This will be confirmed later in the day, as you put the various cast-off bits of scrag end of neck which the butcher let you have on the basis that you will *definitely* be entering into negotiations with a view to discussing how you are going to commence payments aimed at reducing his bill

– and the chippings which were left after all the mouldy bits were cut out of the turnip which that *ever-so-nice* greengrocer man let you pick up from his floor, into the pot for a nice, rewarding, and tasty evening repast.

As you are working away, using your, by now, considerable culinary skills to great advantage, there will be a figure hovering around talking in disjointed phrases:' ... only forty five grand ... for a five year old ... I'll *kill* her ... at her age ... I mean ... forty five grant for a five year old ... Irish Draft Cross Thoroughbred ... only forty five grand ... '

This will go on as you serve up the meal, and pour out the dregs of what was left in your next-door neighbour's Claret bottle which, as luck would have it, you found cast aside by the dustbins that morning.

It will continue through the meal, and beyond, as you relax in the languid evening, leafing through the most recent letters from the Bank Manager, check on the state of the County Court Judgements and deal with the latest batch of the day's final demands.

It will still be forming the undertone of all proceedings as you make for your bed, for perhaps the best proposition of all – the majority of eight hours of reverie without a single horse to trouble your status quo – except perhaps those ones suffering a fate far worse than death at the hands of your dreamland alter ego, the Supreme Dictator of the Universe.

As you close your eyes, and your mind starts to select your Supreme Dictator of the Universe uniform for the night, and you give yourself a Dictator sort of identity and a name such as Adolf Horsehater, your worst possible nightmares are about to begin.

By your side, the litany of disjointed conversation is still continuing, and for a short while, it becomes positively therapeutic, filling the air with an almost mesmeric ability to send you to sleep.

Then, suddenly, you feel a tremendous grasp of your arm and you sit bolt upright in bed.

'Jimmy ... JIMMY!! ... I've GOT IT!!' the voice will say at your side.

'Got *what?*' [Rabies? Walking Horsehater Syndrome? Malaysian Creeping Horsefeed Insanity?]

'I've got the solution.' *I'VE GOT TO HAVE ANOTHER HORSE!!'*

'Oh?' you will groan, pulling the bed clothes over your head, and beginning, in your mind the construction of a VAST horse extermination facility. 'I could have told you that this morning ... '

AT THE HORSE DEALER'S

The decision having been made that you are going to have this second horse, come what may, you will now begin interacting with that special section of horsey people, the *HORSE DEALERS.*

I have alluded to this particular breed of human being when discussing the Horse Lorry Dealers (q.v.), but for those of you who were either asleep at the time or skipped that bit, I will just mention that these are the people who are, in the *VAST MAJORITY OF CASES* such *FINE AND WONDERFUL CITIZENS THAT I HAVE OFTEN WONDERED WHY THE REST OF US UNWORTHY MORTALS DON'T GIVE THEM THE FREEDOM OF EVERY CITY IN THE LAND* but *in the opinion of some members of the public* contain a few individuals who stuck to the ancient ways of the Iceni and continued conning gullible horsey people in horse deals when all the other spivs went on to bigger and more up-to-date technology by selling cars and lorries.

However, coming back to Horse Dealers, it is worth pointing out that these come in two distinct brands – Male ones and Female ones.

The *Male* ones, are, as I said before, *VERY FINE AND UPSTANDING CITIZENS WHO GO ABOUT THEIR BUSINESS IN A VERY FINE AND UPSTANDING SORT OF WAY* but their very fine and upstanding brotherhood is unfortunately tainted here and there *[and only in VERY RARE AND ISOLATED INSTANCES, YOU UNDERSTAND]* by the odd *DIRTY OLD MAN* who makes constant lewd and suggestive remarks to your partner, whether you are in his company or not, and, given half a chance, and more often than not, even given *no* chance, will seek every opportunity to place the palms of his hands in proximity to your loved one's rear end.

Unfortunately for you, even though this type of creep is *UNEQUIVOCALLY AND NOTWITHSTANINDLY AS AFOREMENTIONED M'LUD VERY MUCH IN THE MICRO MINORITY OF THE ARMY OF FINE AND UPSTANDING AND TOTALLY WORTHY AND BLAMELESS HORSE DEALERS*, *every* male horse dealer which you seem to be landed with seems to behave in this manner. It's just the luck of the draw I suppose.

The *FEMALE ONES* are similarly *FINE AND WONDERFUL CITIZENS* in the *VAST MAJORITY OF CASES* but here again, you always seem to find yourself dealing with one who should be avoided at all costs – and, given *your* luck, your partner is more than likely to attempt to buy from one of these, so you are well advised to have adequate supplies of snake venom antidote in the medicine cupboard at home.

Anyhow, the sort of *ISOLATED AND BY NO MEANS REPRESENTATIVE SCENARIO* which will probably befall you goes something like this:

AT THE [ISOLATED EXAMPLE AND TOTALLY UNREPRESENTATIVE] MALE HORSE DEALER

At the [Isolated Example and Totally Unrepresentative] Male Horse Dealer

You arrive along a twisting and difficult, heavily rutted trackway [is there any *other* kind in the horsey world?] which eventually opens out into a stable yard.

As you look around you notice that half dead horses hang their dishevelled heads in desperate disarray over the stable doors and there is an ominous smell of glue coming from beyond a dark passageway in the corner.

Sensing your arrival, a figure emerges from this passageway and walks towards you.

You know he's the Dealer because he wears one of those battered brown trilby hats which seem all the rage in the horsey world – the more the battering, particularly of the brim, the better, it seems. You see hundreds of them at race meetings and wonder if the wearer could only see himself in a mirror away from the racecourse whether he would ever be seen dead in the damn thing, let alone walk about in it trying to look posh.

The Dealer will also have a tattered V-neck cardigan, surmounted by a regulation sports jacket [well mucked, incidentally] and the regulation cavalry twill trousers stuffed into equally well mucked hunter wellies – these by the way are exactly the same as normal wellies, except for the fact that they have a strange looking buckle at the top of each leg which doesn't seem to be performing any practical function – and of course as a result of that they cost fifteen times more than normal wellies – but I guess you were expecting that by now.

The flies of his trousers will be undone, but he won't give a toss for that, and he will be walking towards you with that curious 'John Wayne' sort of gait, all bow-legged and scratching his groin before picking his nose with the self same hand he will then extend to shake yours.

Your partner will open: 'Have you got any horses for sale?'

He will reply: 'Who wants to sell horses when I can give you a good shagging, moi deer?' [incidentally the use of 'moi' instead of the more usual 'my' is his attempt to sound vaguely 'country' even though he probably emanates from somewhere like Walsall. This is an attempt to give himself a sort of 'farmerish' credibility, so that all his lewd speech and disgusting antics will be ignored, because gits from the city, like you, *always* have a condescending attitude towards japey old rustics with their country ways and their charming pokey unsophisticated charm which, if practised anywhere else would inevitably lead to a remand under the Vagrancy Act].

'I'm looking for a 16.2 or 16.3, maybe a gelding, or maybe a mare... do you have anything like that at the moment?'

'Cor, you've got a nice pair of tits. Oi wouldn't moind gettin' me 'ands around *those* nubblers moi deer...'

He will then turn to you, as if to draw you to one side and whisper: 'How much to *bugger off* for twenty minutes or so... oi'll make it worth your while...'

All through this, both you and your partner will try with your best endeavours to ignore this lewd behaviour, chalking it up, in your mind, to the sort of stuff you have to endure – they're all like this, so this pratt isn't any different from the rest sort of thing...so you will just have to put up with it until such time as he get on to the *subject* in *hand,* rather than what he would like to get *in* his hand. You will feel that you are succeeding when he appears to be returning to the subject of selling you a horse.

Wiping his brow with the palm of his hand, he will look across the gallery of flagging nags in front of him and say something like: ' . . . a 16.2 is it you're after?'

'Yes,' your partner will say, 'or a 16.3'

'Well, there's Charlie over there. He's a 16.2. Do you want to 'ave a look at 'im?'

At that, he will lead your partner towards the stable, motioning to you, if you were so bold as to follow, with some sort of gesture which roughly interpreted would say something like: 'Can't you take the hint and bugger off?'

You will be somewhat surprised to see the gesture of his hand indicating that your partner should enter the stable – you never realised that a palm placed strategically on her bum meant *that,* and you will be equally bemused that, once they have entered, the top of the stable door seems to swing shut of its own accord.

For a few moments, you will hear a muttering of muffled voices, then a female voice raised in anger saying something like *'TAKE YOUR BLOODY HAND AWAY, I'M **WARNING** YOU!!!'* followed by the sound of some sort of impact, and a suppressed yelp.

The next you will see will be the stable door opening so fast that it almost comes off its hinges, your partner emerging, looking very business like and somewhat stern, followed some moments later by a rather red-face Horse Dealer, now curiously minus his John Wayne gait and instead adopting a stooped and knees-together sort of stagger, with his hand once more at his groin, though not appearing to be exactly *scratching* it this time around.

As your partner gets back into the car without another word, you may offer something along the lines of: ' I take it Charlie wasn't *quite* what you were looking for, then??'

AT THE [ISOLATED EXAMPLE AND TOTALLY UNREPRESENTATIVE] FEMALE HORSE DEALER

After such an incident, you will notice that all the horse dealers you see from now on appear to be women.

This will be an essentially different kind of experience and this is the sort of **ISOLATED AND BY NO MEANS REPRESENTATIVE SCENARIO** which may befall you:

You will notice immediately that there is a distinct change of attitude to the totally untypical and isolated experience you seem to have had every time you went to see a male horse dealer. This will be apparent as soon as you get out of the car and observe the dealer across the other side of the yard. She will be busying herself with something useful, like trying to glue back the hind leg onto a horse, or fitting a new wig onto a stuffed stallion to make it look as though it's really alive.

She won't acknowledge your arrival, nor even your presence as you stroll over to her and say something like: 'Are you the horse dealer?'

After repeating this question for twenty or so times, you will finally get the reply: 'Who wants to know?' and then, somewhat furtively, you note: 'You're not from the *Inland Revenue* are you?'

'No,' your partner will say, taking the initiative. 'I'm, Helen Squib . . . I rang . . . remember . . . ?'

At that, the horse dealer will lighten up a little and say something like: 'Oh . . . yes . . . of course . . . you . . . want to buy a horse . . . you **sure** you're not from the Revenue?'

'No . . . I just want to buy a horse.'

Looking in your direction the horse dealer will say: 'What about him? Looks like a VAT man to me.'

'No . . . no . . .' you will say, extending your hand which will not be accepted: 'I'm Jimmy Squib, I'm Helen's . . .'

' . . . non horsey other half,' your partner will helpfully complete for you. Isn't that *kind* of her?

Still eyeing you with suspicion, the horse dealer will say, as though probing a little deeper into your bona fides: 'Who recommended you to come to me, then?'

'Val Twistleton-Twistleton.'

There will be a narrowing of the brow, a look as though brain is in search mode then a lightening of the features.

'Oh . . . yes . . . I sold her a horse . . . I think . . .'

'Yes. You did, about four months ago . . .'

At that the features will darken again.

'How is he . . . the *horse* I mean. How's he getting along?'

'Oh fine. Val won the Intermediate Out of Hand Round and Round the Garden Like a Teddy Bear Hunter March and Moorland Three Day Dressage on him at Billy Baffin Land's place the other week – largely on account of the fact that she was the only entrant, but it was a red rosette nevertheless.'

A curious inquisitorial look will then come into the horse dealer's eyes: 'So he's *still alive* then?'

'Very much so'

'And how about the legs? Still got all four?'

'Yes' – and here the first look of suspicion will begin to creep into your partner's conversation: 'Why are you so interested?'

'O h . . . no reason really . . . I . . . er . . . always *knew* that one would do well . . . it was his breeding. Let him go far too cheaply in the end, but that's always my trouble. Too kind hearted, you see. 'Cause you understand that I'm not really a dealer, no matter what Val might have said. I only dabble – buying one for my own use and then letting him go to a good home. Then getting another.'

At that your gaze may range across the hundred or so stable doors surrounding you, each of which has a horse's head poking out of it with a sign saying 'For Sale' and marvel that this non-dealer type person has so much time on her hands that she can have so many horses for her own personal use.

Anyhow, the non-dealer will then say something like: 'What are you looking for?'

At which your partner will then trot out the requirements in some detail, bringing that second look of suspicion, this time across the non-dealer's features.

'You seem to know *quite a bit* about horses . . .'

To which your partner [and to your *dismay*] will look to the floor and look humble and say something like: 'Oh. I've picked up a few hints here and there.'

To which the non-dealer will say: 'Got a horse already, or not?'

To which you will, in some sort of ridiculous air of trying to get in on the conversation I thought we had covered that by now and you had learned your lesson well and truly, but there we are] will pipe up with:

'Yes . . . his name's Dodo and he's the love of her life'

As you nurse the rapidly developing bruise on your shin, the conversation will continue between partner and non-dealer, who will now be eyeing each other with the same look that two lionesses have when they are just about to tear each other apart.

The non-dealer, realising that she is non-dealing with someone who knows *everything* there is ever to be known about horses, will be back-tracking at break-neck speed.

'16.2 or 16.3 your say . . . no . . . I don't think I've got anything like that at the moment. You see, as I said, I don't really *deal* in horses as such – and anyone who said that I did is a liar and if I ever catch up with them I'll have them summonsed for slander, or else I'll get my Ernie to beat them up. You see . . . I've only got a couple of ponies in at the moment – and they're not for sale.'

Your partner, now in predatory mode, will motion towards a herd of 16.2's in the adjoining field.

'They look like 16.2's to me . . .'

'Oh . . . yes . . . they are . . . how astute of you to notice, you smart arsed bitch . . . but they're not for sale . . . in fact they're nothing to do with me . . .'

'So why have they got a 'For Sale' sign on the gate?'

'Oh . . . *that* . . . Put there as a joke, I expect. It's amazing the practical jokes that our Ernie gets up to . . . er . . . actually I'm looking after those for a friend of mine who's on holiday at the minute, if you must know.'

At that moment, a loud horn blast will summon the non-dealer to address the arrival of a horse lorry which has turned into the yard. An extremely angry looking man will rapidly be leading out a three legged horse from the back.

The non-dealer will try her best to remain nonchalant, and indifferent to this arrival, even re-running the same routine you were treated to when this man demands to know whether she is the horse dealer.

Her attempts at the 'Who wants to know?' routine will be summarily cut short however by the appearance of a woman, equally red faced as the man, with tears streaming down her face and pointing an accusing finger in the non-dealer's direction.

'That's her, Barry,' you will hear her say. 'That's the one . . .'

As you try in our own way to make for your getaway, you will not fail to hear the man saying something like: 'My wife bought this horse from you last week as a sound pedigree Thoroughbred which you said was eight years old and had the makings of a particularly good In Hand Hunter Zambesi Rules Frilly Knickers Dressage Trials Competitor, we paid you £67,000 cash and last night its bloody back leg dropped off – *SO WHAT ARE YOU GOING TO DO ABOUT IT!!!*'

You will note a curious feeling of almost admiration for the non-dealer as she flies into a total rage, waving her arms about and frothing at the mouth and babbling inanely as she accuses them of 'slander' and 'libel' and 'I'm going to get my solicitor on to you *right now*' and 'you'll be laughing on the other side of your face when my solicitor bangs you up in the maximum security wing of Dartmoor Prison after he's got you convicted of this *slanderious libel*' and 'anyway I'm going to get my Ernie round your place and have you beaten up . . .'

Then, to your horror, the non-dealer will drag hold of you and babble: 'look, here's my witness . . . you saw what he said didn't you . . . don't you think I should get my solicitor on to him right now and get Ernie to beat him up? I tell you what, you stand there and I'll go and get on the phone to my solicitor right away . . .'

At that, she will disappear into a nearby house, leaving you to face a man who clearly believes that you are something to do with the non-dealer. And he's none too pleased.

You will also note, that as he turns to vent his wrath in your direction, you detect something you hadn't really noticed before – that his voice has a distinct accent to it. Distinctly . . . er . . . *East End of London* type of thing.

Your demeanour will not be enhanced by reading the badge on the side of the lorry, which you now note is one of those *'Palaces on Wheels'* jobs which clearly features a rather large integral cocktail bar in the living compartment, and which displays on its doors details that this person is involved in the amusement arcade and night club profession and is located in the Essex area.

It will be at this point that you realise the numbers standing in the yard are now beginning to swell, with the addition of two rather large blokes who have exited rather untidily from the back of the *'Palace on Wheels'*. At the same time, you will begin to wonder how long it takes a non-dealer, who, you will recall, you've never clapped eyes on before this day, to make a simple telephone call to a solicitor. Then you will recall that this is a Sunday, and marvel at the fact that the *non-dealer's* solicitor seems to be the *only one in* the entire universe who is easily accessible on a Sunday.

Looking for the support of your partner, you will realise that she had been successful in her escape and is sitting, quite snugly, in the car reading the Horse and Hound or some other prescribed reading, and with her head thus buried in the magazine, will be unaware of your impending doom.

The only advice I can offer in this sort of a situation is:

BLOODY WELL SCARPER

and hope that the growing of a moustache and adoption of a new hair style manages to change your overall appearance sufficiently so that you would not be recognised again by any of these people.

Your partner, as usual, will be the tower of strength that you always need in moments such as this. She will no doubt stir slightly as you fumble with the keys and with trembling hands desperately attempt to get the car going.

'You seem to be in a hurry,' she will mutter, while lazily enjoying the comfort of a chocolate bar and flicking the pages of her magazine.

Terror will prevent an answer. It will also be a useful palliative to the pain you would otherwise suffer at gouging out a huge chunk of the offside wing of the car as you collide with a gate post in your haste to get back to safety.

At that, she might even look up from the magazine and mutter: 'Steady on . . . you almost made me bite my tongue . . .'

But you will know you are returning to normality as you break free onto open roads again and civilisation begins to loom in your direction to the accompaniment from your partner of: 'What do you think of this? – 16.2 sound pedigree Thoroughbred, eight years old, has the makings of a particularly good In Hand Hunter Zambesi Rules Frilly Knickers Dressage Trials Competitor. A Steal at £67,000. – Sounds Interesting.'

To which you will, somewhat smugly reply: 'I think you will find that the telephone number on the ad is somewhat familiar.'

Your partner will look again and then, somewhat put out say something like: 'Oh, who's the clever dick, then. How did you know? Been peeking at my Horse and Hound?'

'No dear, just intuition, I suppose.'

Some days later, you may be interested as you pick up the paper to read that someone answering to the name 'Ernie' who had previously been reported missing, had been found naked and wandering in a dazed and confused state, somewhere in the Chelmsford area.

THE HOMECOMING OF
HORSE NUMBER TWO

The fact that a second horse comes into your life is only a matter of time. No matter how many encounters and rumpy-pumpy attempts in closed stables there are with bent and crooked people who should be locked up and the keys thrown away into the deepest parts of the ocean, you will eventually be presented with horse number two.

More than likely, it won't come from a dealer. It will be provided via the jungle telegraph of the horsey world, such that one night, as you doze, issuing your 500th anti-horse edict in your part time dreamworld role as Adolf Horsehater, Supreme Dictator of the Entire Universe, a loud and persistent knocking on the front door will rouse you and your partner from your respective slumbers.

On opening the front door, you will be confronted by a round faced lady of not too obscure appearance, who will say something like: 'Helen Squib?'

'You'll want my wife,' you will stupidly say [For God's sake, she could hardly take a vagrant like you in this tatty and hung over condition for a woman could she???]

Whereupon, your partner will appear and the conversation will go something like this:

'Helen Squib?'

'Yes'

'I'm Mandy. Mandy Horsefeeds-Cheesecakes. I'm a friend of a friend of a sister of a niece of a friend of a direct Darwinian descendent of a friend of Val Twistleton-Twistleton's estranged daughter's baby-sitter. I understand that you are looking for a 16.2 Irish Draft Cross Thoroughbred?'

'Yes. I am.'

'I have one in the back of the lorry at the moment.'

DON'T at this point make any reference to the time – which is probably pushing three in the morning.

'You have him in the back of the lorry?'

'Yes. When we heard of your plight we came straight down.'

'From where?' you might interject – after all it's a free country and if you want to get in on this conversation, then you have **every right to do so.**

'Muck.'

'Of course,' you will find yourself saying, 'but there's no real need to be offensive, it was a simple enough enquiry...'

'Yes ... Muck ... in the Outer Hebrides?' Mandy will helpfully reply.

'Oh ... *that* Muck. You've come a long way.'

'Yes, it's taken us three days of solid driving. I hope after all this that he's what you're looking for.'

'I'm *sure* he will be,' your partner will enthuse. 'In fact, I don't think there's any point in even seeing him. **WE'LL HAVE HIM, WON'T WE JIMMY DARLING.'**

At which Mandy, who is still standing on the doorstep will look somewhat darkly towards you.

'Well ... it's not really as *straightforward* as that, is it? After all, I have to be *absolutely* **sure** that my lovely boy is coming to a good home.'

You may get a little puffed up and pear shaped at this and splutter: 'Now hang on a minute... Helen knows *everything* there is *ever likely to be* known by *anyone* in the *entire universe* about horses – **and what's more** she won the Ashmolean Museum Hanky Panky Unnatural Massage [**Dressage** you fool, it's called **Dressage** ... **Massage** is, well, something *else*]

A severe stab to the rear of your knee cap will be followed swiftly by: 'You'll have to forgive Jimmy, Mandy.'

To which Mandy will reply in that sort of benign, avuncular, all-knowing sort of way: 'He's your non-horsey other half, am I right? [leaving a moment's pause for the unsaid ' and you have my **deepest sympathies,** my dear].

'Yes,' you will hear your partner sigh [leaving another pause into which she might be thinking: 'Oh Mandy – is there *any* hope for him????]. Then she will add: 'Anyway, forget everything he was drivelling on about. Of course I understand that you would wish to learn a little about us before letting him come to us. What do you suggest we do?'

Mandy will then beckon towards the lorry parked on your drive from which will emerge a whole army of people.

'I thought it best to get this over with a quickly as possible, after all, from what I can gather from my friend's sister's niece's friend's direct Darwinian descendant's friend of Val Twistleton-

Twistleton's estranged daughter's baby-sitter, you are a pretty good and safe bet, but it is always wise to be sure – so I've just brought along a few of my people so that we can get this all wrapped up tonight.'

What will follow will be an eight hour grilling from people who turn out to be ex-members of the Special Branch, the Serious Fraud Office, the Customs and Excise (Special Investigation) Section, a team of Doctors, a Traffic Warden, Dog Warden, School Patrol Warden, Big Game Warden, Butlin's Red Coat, Transvestite Hairdresser, Dog Trainer, Lion Tamer, Italian

Engineering Mechanic who specialises in Left Handed Screw Assemblies, a Vicar, a Papal Nuncio, a clockwork expert [he'll be particularly interested in your growing collection of clockwork models of Freddy Farquarson Farquar, by the way, so have them all handy] Horse Feed Nutritionist, Intensive one-to-one Counsellor, Highlands and Islands District Councillor, a King George V Look-Alike Contest Winner of 1932, Accountant, Liquidation Practitioner and a member of Her Majesty's Drainage Inspectorate.

In those short eight hours, you will never know that you have done so many things you ought not to have done, not done so many things you ought to have done, have erred and strayed from thy almighty ways like lost sheep and there is hardly any health in you etc etc.

Your bank accounts will be scrutinised via clever little devices which can tap into the most sensitive information in your bank files, which will lead you to wonder why the Bank Manager's appointments with your partner always seem to be *outside* normal banking hours.

A cunning little chap who turns out to be a serving member of the SAS will scale your drainpipes along with Her Majesty's Drainage Inspector to make sure that there is absolutely no possibility of terrorists using your place as a base – this might upset the horse, you understand – while the Serious Fraud People will grill you incessantly about that extra ten pence you put on your expenses without a supporting docket back in 1975 – oh yes, they know *all* about *you* chummy!

The Doctors will give you and your partner a thorough medical going over – though once they have been assured that you have Non-Horsey Other-Half Status they will go easy on the amount of booze you throw down your system.

You will then have to sign a declaration that you are both non-smokers, and that you adopt a non-sexist, non-racist, totally Politically Correct attitude towards everything – except of course non-horsey people who are the slimeballs of the earth and who should be sent back to wherever they came from on the first Banana Boat going.

At the end of all of this, Mandy will draw together all the data on the mainframe computer which the ever-so-helpful computer team from IBM managed to get up and running in time, organise a satellite link up with an Australian based mainframe which can provide the last little chink of information about the whereabouts of your Great Uncle in 1963, and then, with satisfaction declare that you are *absolutely* the right sort to have the horse.

HALL-EL-U-JAH HALL-EL-U-JAH HALL-EL-U-JAH HALL-EL-U-JAH

HA-LEY-LU-YAHHHHHHHHHHHHH!!!

With relief, you will reach for the box of matches in order to find a couple so that you can prop your eyes open, while your partner uses the opportunity to ask a couple of questions of her own:

'What's his name?'

'Percy Peregrine Petula Patricia Petronella Pinky Parcels V'

'What's his other name?'

'Oh, you can call him **POOCHIE**'

And so, as Mandy and her entourage take their leave of you, and the Band of the Royal Scots Dragoon Guards, who have been waiting outside all night in anticipation, pipe a general retreat, you get your first glimpse of the new entity who has come into your life, to cause you all the trouble, strife, heartache, pain, mental torment, and general downright depressing desperate derision – and now it's going to be twice as bad, because **THERE ARE TWO OF THE BLOODY THINGS.**

POOCHIE MEETS DODO

The first thing to remember about Poochie is that he will *never under any circumstances* be better, or command any greater proportion of your partner's affections than Dodo. Dodo is the eternal god. Mummy's little incey wincey little boy. Poochie, on the other hand is, well *nice* but nowhere near as nice as Dodo.

He will still be miles ahead of you, though, so don't think that the arrival of this nag into your life will give you any added status in the family pecking order. In fact, you move one place back – behind Dodo, of course, then Poochie, newly elevated into **second place,** then any sundry farm animals that might be lurking around your kitchen, the dog, the kitten, the budgies, hamsters, rabbit, Lithuanian Swamp Toad, Uncle Jarvis's stuffed fish, the aspidistra and the spiders who infest your curtain tracks. Then you. On a good day that is.

But the fact that he isn't *quite* on the same status level as Dodo means that your partner will have a very curious attitude towards him. She definitely *wants* Poochie, but she also definitely *doesn't* want him either.

She wants him, not withstanding the fact that she has to keep up with Di who doesn't know the first thing about horses, because he is needed as a companion to Dodo, whom he will one day replace.

But she *doesn't* want him because all she really wants is Dodo, and anyway why should she have to *replace* Dodo. Can't Dodo be granted some sort of divine dispensation and be allowed to live for ever?

So poor old Poochie has to behave exceptionally well at all times, because any fall from grace means that he will *definitely* have to be sold. 'There's no getting away from it, he will *have to go*. Why on earth I ever allowed you to suggest having him in the first place, I'll never know.'

This will last until the next day when he behaves himself once more. You will know everything has rectified itself when your partner sidles up to you with a broad look of love and contentment on her face, throws her arms around you and says: 'Jimmy... oh Jimmy... my dearest, dearest darling, I just **LOVE** Poochie.'

The second fact that you must always bear in mind about Poochie is that Dodo hates him. He hates the very ground he stands upon, he hates the air Poochie breathes, he hates the water Poochie drinks from the water trough and the very grass which gives rise to Poochie's first attack of laminitis.

But remember, he still hates *you* even more, so don't delude yourself that somehow by having a common enemy you can achieve some measure of redress in the way you are treated. It doesn't quite *work* that way.

In fact, given a clash of personalities, Dodo will *always* take Poochie's part against you – until that is, you are well and truly out of the way, and then he will start kicking all hell out of Poochie again.

In short, therefore, the most you can ever expect is a sort of love-hate relationship. *You* will offer *love,* friendship, understanding, companionship and all that slushy sort of stuff to your partner, Dodo and Poochie [as well as all the rest of the aforementioned menagerie]. *They* in return, will simply *hate* you.

Knowing this is of no great use to you, I'm afraid, at the tense and traumatic first meeting of Poochie and Dodo. Such an event is best avoided at all costs, but, as you have just accepted your Bank Manager's suggestion that you should *really* take up a very interesting fund raising opportunity involving just a few late night hours of your services strolling about the inner city areas in a rather natty little velvet suit with rather unusual tight shorts and curious leather flat peaked cap which for some reason is decorated in chains, and carrying a notice board declaring: GET IT HERE – JUST 20 QUID – in order to raise money towards the fifty grand which Poochie has cost, you will no doubt be deluded into thinking that somehow you *should* be present as the clash of the titans takes place, if for no other reason than to protect your Bank Manager's investment.

I've seen grown men reduced to tears on such occasions, believe me.

The first notification that something is decidedly wrong will register in Dodo's mind on the arrival of the horse lorry. At first he may assume that he is due to go somewhere and do his vanishing act again.

But then, he will hear the sound of something which sounds ominously like *another horse.*

As soon as the lorry ramp is down, his worst fears will be confirmed. There, standing before him will be Poochie.

You will know he's not altogether too pleased about all of this by the sound of the loud stamping on the ground from his hooves, and the snorting sound coming out of his nostrils. Further confirmation will come from the rather quaint way he kicks your shin when you are ordered to try to bring him under control.

At that he will be off again, and you may feel that he has done just the right thing, and moreover, given you and your partner the time you need to get Poochie out of the lorry and into the field.

Not so. The very moment Poochie enters the hallowed turf of the hitherto exclusively occupied field, Dodo will be back again, snorting, stamping, kicking, bucking wildly in every direction imaginable – though mostly in yours.

Poochie, for his part, will cotton on to what is happening and join in the fun, leaping about, snorting and demonstrating his glee at being cooped up with this pampered bastard, the sight of whom he hates with as much reciprocal venom.

After landing a kick on your other shin, Poochie will lead the way, with a wild gallop far off into the distance, with Dodo in train attempting to land wild and malicious hoof prints all over his frame.

Close by you will hear an excited voice: 'Jimmy. . . *I think they really like each other.'*

About an hour or two later, two bedraggled forms will hobble down the field towards you oozing blood from gashes about their heads, shoulders, legs, and hind quarters. Exhausted from their 'nice to get to know you' party, they will just about be able to stand as they receive the plaudits from your partner: ' . . . there you are my lovely boys . . . I just *knew* you'd make friends . . . it was just a matter of time . . . we are all going to be so *very very happy* together . . . I just *know* it . . .'

Wondering whether you should really be going down to the Casualty Department of the local Hospital for a couple of plaster casts on your shins – the pain hasn't seemed to diminish this time like it usually does – you will then sense a sudden change in your partner's reaction.

It will come with the time honoured opener: 'Oh bugger!'

'What's the matter?' you will say through gritted teeth, trying manfully to beat the pain threshold and not sound too bothered.

'It look's like we're going to have to get the Vet in tomorrow. Poochie's kicked Dodo's withers, and Dodo's caused a nasty little gash on Poochie's hock. It'll mean that I won't be able to ride either of them for six weeks . . .'

AT THE HOSPITAL CASUALTY DEPARTMENT

One of the inevitabilities of the horse world is that sooner or later, your partner will have an accident serious enough to warrant banging her up in hospital [the **General Accident** and **Orthopaedic** kind, that is, not the other sort which you now know she should have been banged up in years ago for her own protection]

Hospitalisation injuries are another of the essential aspects of the horsey world. Just as at any one time more than half of the acting profession is 'resting' [i.e. **unemployed**] so at any one time more than half of the horsey people are also 'resting' [i.e. either *in* hospital having just received injuries, or *just out* of hospital in various states of recovery]

It's entirely logical when you come to think of it – which I am sure you now see with the benefit of the knowledge which I trust you have managed to gain from this little guide.

Only the barmy would take part in a practice which pays them nothing, costs them [sorry, *you*] a king's ransom while being genuinely risky to life and limb. Only the ultra barmy [and horsey people] go on taking part in this activity week in, week out, and seem to revel in it as the injuries continue to mount and as various parts of their anatomies seem systematically to disappear.

And, come to think of it, injury is the final satisfaction which the horses can meet out on these barmy people – not only does it inflict maximum physical pain, but also ensures an extended period of not being ridden.

Anyway, you will get your first indication that something of this nature has taken place when you receive the first of many many early morning phone calls.

'Jimmy...Jimmy...I've...had an accident...but it wasn't Dodo's fault...you've **got** to understand that... it wasn't Dodo's fault, so you'd better just put out of your mind any thought of blaming him... it was **all my fault** and I **totally deserve** everything I got...now I can understand it if it was Poochie, after all... he's only been with us for five minutes...takes time to settle into my ways...so it would have been perfectly understandable if it were Poochie... *BUT HOW DARE YOU SUGGEST IT WAS DODO'S FAULT!!!!...THAT'S THE TROUBLE WITH YOU, ALWAYS BLAMING POOR LITTLE DODO-KINS*...Dodo's a **real little darling who loves his mummy**...so how **could** you even contemplate such a thing...no *I* am to blame...it was **entirely my fault**...understand...the fault lies fairly and squarely with *me*...Jimmy...I thought better of you to think that it was in any way shape or form dear little Dodo's fault...'

This, by the way may go on for some hours before you establish such irrelevant facts such as

At the Hospital Casualty Department

1. Exactly *what* happened

2. *Where* it happened

3. *Where* she is now

4. How *bad* is the injury etc etc

But by now I assume you will know enough to realise that this is entirely secondary to the most important task- that of establishing Dodo's innocence beyond question [even though the accident was caused by the bastard shying at a stuffed aadvark at the side of the road and taking off uncontrollably for a few miles before unceremoniously dumping your partner in a cess pit conveniently located in Billy Baffin Land's Piggery]

If this is your first encounter with an accident of this nature, it is extremely important to understand that Dodo cannot possibly be at fault, and also to **stay calm,** otherwise you might fall into the trap of losing control and gushing out crap like:'Oh FOR GOD'S SAKE HELEN ARE YOU *ALRIGHT?????* ARE YOU ALIVE . . . IS IT *LIFE THREATENING* . . . Oh my GOD, WHAT ARE WE GOING TO DO?????? DARLING JUST STAY THERE ON THE LINE AND FOR PITY'S SAKE *STAY ALIVE*' . . . and all that sort of low grade Australian soap opera guff.

If it's *not* your first time then you will be well seasoned to the routine by now and know that it is simply a matter of waiting until she has allowed you to get a word in edgeways so that you can reassure her that in no way do you believe or could be led to believe that the fault lay at Dodo's door, and then probably add something like: 'Which hospital is nearest? Oh yes . . . there again . . . I wonder if those rather nice rose bushes in the garden next to the fracture clinic are blooming at the moment. Do you remember that Administrator I got rather pally with said I could take a cutting if we came back when they were blooming? Let's see, it's Clive who's the surgeon there – shall I give him a call and tell him you're on your way? How long do you reckon you'll be in for this time? Is this a three, four or five week one? Where did you put the hospital bag? Didn't you put it in the cupboard under the stairs the last time you came out? Funny old life isn't it, I only got a new tube of toothpaste this morning, so I'll make sure I'll pack it. I had a funny feeling that it was going to come in handy. And come to think of it, could you tell me the whereabouts of the home made jam? If you recall, Clive said he wanted a jar when you were next in his tender care. By the way, what is it this time? Ankle, knee, leg or elbow? Or is it one of those interesting combination jobs?'

Then, on reaching the scene of this calamitous event, you will see your partner, nursing whatever has been crushed, broken, battered or simply destroyed, and in the company of a very helpful ambulanceman and the conversation will go something like this:

'Hello, Jimmy – she's been at it again, then. Where to this time?'

142

'Hi, Ken – I think she's going to Clive's place.'

'Oh yes. Of course.'

Then, as he and his mate load your partner into the back of the van, he will no doubt turn round to you with a thankful gesture.

'You know, if it wasn't for good'uns like your wife, the ambulance service in this area would probably be severely cut. They're keeping Frank and me in a job, you know... By the way, any chance of another jar of that delicious home made jam, we've almost come to the end of the last pot...'

The ambulance will then whisk your partner off to Clive's place while you will follow behind, having already organised someone from the army of know-it-all horsey people who are on permanent standby for accidents and emergencies to take care of the wonderful Dodo, who will leave the scene rather like a victorious gladiator sporting a rather curious smug grin all over his face.

If, on the other hand, this is your first experience of the injury routine, you will still no doubt be in distraut low grade Australian soap opera mode, blaming Dodo [**DON'T DO THAT, REMEMBER**], blaming yourself [**YES, THAT'S DEFINITELY OK**], blaming the fact that it's Sunday... 'I should NEVER have let you go out this morning... OH MY GOD WHAT **HAVE I DONE!!!**' sort of stuff.

If this is the case, then perhaps I should give you a few pointers on what happens now.

On arrival at the Hospital Casualty Department you will be ushered into the main reception area where there will be hundreds of pathetic groaning souls doing their best to take care of whatever injuries they have. If this is your first time, then do not be surprised to see that most of these sad people seem to be sporting jods, boots and hacking jackets.

However on *no account* at this point give off the impression that it *is* your first time. Suppress the '**OH MY GODs**' at all costs, because you will inevitably attract the attention of one of those bossy-know-it-all-'actually-I'm-only-one-down-from-God-Almighty-himself' sort of medics who tend to walk round these places in predatory white coats looking important and wearing waspish expressions as they stalk the corridors seeming to be in some sort of eternal mission to make sure that everyone who finds themselves in a place like this has to be *severely chastised* for doing whatever they have done to get in here. Without realising in their innate zeal that if there weren't a whole load of barmy twerps from the horsey fraternity constantly putting themselves in a place like this in the first place then they would no doubt be out of a job and working as a dentist's assistant somewhere, mixing tooth fillings.

Yes, I am well aware of the fact that in this case, you would probably *thoroughly agree* with them and in fact some of you might even consider finding a discarded white jacket, sticking a stethoscope around your neck and joining in haranguing the wailing majority.

But remember that *they* are patients, and in the main, even these type of medical people don't seek to vent their spleen at the barminess of their behaviour. What they are *really* after is the people that are obviously *not* in need of medical care right now, but whom they consider to be part of the whole barmy army and are therefore in line for a sound telling off, because they are equally to blame.

That's why they look out for people like you, because for all they know you are just another horsey person who just happens to be active at the moment rather than 'resting' and this is why you must at such times look sort of *experienced, worldly wise, been through all this several times before, so it's no good having a go at me, matey!!!.*

If, you're successful in this deception they will leave you alone, because they will reckon that at some time in the dim distant past you must have had the sound telling off, and it obviously didn't do you any good and therefore you must be in the mega barmy class and therefore there is no point in them wasting any time or energy on you.

If on the other hand, you're *not* successful in deceiving them – and remember here that they are looking out for that tell tale sign of a little affection towards your partner, or the occasional tear of worry, or, if best comes to the best, the breaking into a cold sweat coupled with a 'OH MY GOD how on earth could this have happened to us' kind of pullarva, then I'm afraid the following is what you are in for:

Just as you are getting a can of pop from the machine [the mere fact that you have probably had to scout around for the change to put in the machine in the first place, rather than delving into the contingency fund of coins that a more experienced person keeps specifically for these occasions, is, I'm afraid, a great give away to your 'first time' status] you will feel a rather nasty little poke on your shoulder.

On turning round, you will be confronted by the bossy-know-it-all-'actually-I'm-only-one-down-from-God-Almighty-himself' medic who, without further ado will lay into you with: 'You horsey people . . . you're all barmy to go on like this . . . you should be ashamed of yourselves . . . when you think of all the time trouble and resources of the NHS which are just WASTED on the likes of you . . . and all you do is go and do it all over again, and then do it again, again. I get just SICK AND FED UP with you. There should be a law passed against all horse riding . . . or else the surgeon should cut your legs off on the first occasion you come in here so that you can't ride the bloody things . . . have you EVER considered how much you are costing the NHS, the taxpayer and the medical profession with this continuing barminess??? *WELL HAVE YOU?????* [he'll be getting quite hysterical by now and start hitting you around the head with a rather large tome which, between blows, you may be able to perceive is called 'The Effects on the Finances of the National Health Service if People Stopped Riding Horses' and it will be at that point the more astute amongst you will begin to realise that you are in for some pretty serious statistics] . . . 400 new beds in acute medicine in Milton Keynes ALONE . . . the ability to put a general hospital at the bottom of EVERYONE'S GARDEN . . . 5 MILLION new doctors . . . training in medicine for the ENTIRE POPULATION OF GHANA . . . just think of what we can do for people who are REALLY ILL, not just GONE IN THE HEAD . . .'

Yes, I know, as I said before, you agree wholeheartedly with this git, but he's only saying it in the context that he thinks *you* are a horsey person and therefore he won't let you have a word in edgeways to give him your point of view.

But I can assure you that this is by far the best situation to be in should you be daft enough to allow yourself to get into such a confrontation in the first place. What you must do is just stand there and take it, and take comfort in the many sympathetic looks you will now be getting from non-horsey other halves and even the odd injured horse person [YES *EVEN THEM!!!*] who recognise that you are taking it for everyone one in the room, in a sort of 'Jack-Hawkins-down-to-earth-honest-working-class-hero-bloke' sort of way. Someone might even delve into his own contingency fund of coins he keeps just for occasions like these, and actually BUY you the can of pop, so there is much to be gained.

What you *MUST NOT DO*, however, is try to speak, because if you did manage to squeeze a few words in, along the lines of: 'Yes, Mr bossy-know-it-all-'actually-I'm-only-one-down-from-God-Almighty-himself sort of medic bloke, I ABSOLUTELY AGREE WITH YOU, I HAVEN'T HEARD SO MUCH SENSE FOR YEARS' all that you will get for your trouble is a strange and terrified look from this person, and the immediate summoning of a straight jacket which will be used to cart you off to the psychiatric padded cells where you could undergo months, if not years of medical experimentation.

You see, he will think that he has finally found an extremely rare entity – a horsey person who *admits* to a medical man that he really *is* barmy -and therefore it is only logical that he takes the appropriate action.

This, as I say, is only a word of warning to those of you undergoing your first experience of Casualty. For the rest of us, Casualty has become a sort of second social club, so once you get into the swing of things, it can actually become quite enjoyable.

Most of the awaiting patients will greet your partner with: 'Hello, Helen, what's your's this time?' while most of the awaiting staff will greet you with the: 'Hello Jimmy's' and some may even follow up with: 'I'm glad you're back with us again in a way because I'm running down to my last spoonful of your mother's excellent home made jam – you haven't a spare jar have you?' [Come on, hands up how many of you thought that the jam had been made by Helen??? – you ought to *know* by *now*]

From hereon, Casualty will follow the same old familiar pattern. You will wait around for ages

145

until it's your turn, then there will be the routine of the Casualty Doctor taking a swift look at the X-Rays, shaking his head and tutting and looking somewhat concerned.

The patter will then follow a well trodden pathway:

'Oh dear, dear, dear . . . it looks like you've shattered your left elbow this time, Helen.'

'Is it bad, Alan?'

'It's not good. Looks like there is a good chance you might never be able to use your left arm again for anything useful.'

At that your partner will grip your arm with her right hand and burst into tears. The scene will take on the mantle of one of those American hospital dramas where everyone talks in meaningless medical terms because it sounds good and get the ratings up.

'What are you saying to me, Alan?'

The Doctor will shake his head.

'Mrs Squib . . . er . . . Helen . . . what I'm saying is that it looks pretty bad. It looks like you've got an acute carcinogenic avuncular thespian underpass of the left ventricular subdural haematomic occipital lobe. Obviously I will have to wait for the opinion of Mr Tombstone the Consultant, but it looks the way it's shaping up, according to the X-Rays.'

'But . . . but . . . but Clive *always* deals with it. And he's always made it OK.'

'Yes, but listen to what I'm saying. You have really badly shattered it this time [then in a tone as though he's actually *auditioning* for the aforementioned American hospital drama] You . . . might . . . never . . . be . . . able . . . to . . . use . . . your . . . arm . . . again . . .'

'So what you're saying is that [there are copious tears and tuggings at your arm with her right hand at this point] *I MIGHT NEVER RIDE AGAIN???????!!!!!! IS THAT WHAT YOU MEAN?????? JUST GIVE IT TO ME STRAIGHT, ALAN. YOU KNOW I CAN TAKE IT!!!! JUST GIVE IT TO ME RIGHT BETWEEN THE EYES NO HOLDS BARRED . . .*'

'Oh, you'll be able to ride again. No problem. It's just the rest of your life which will be messed up.'

At which a ray of sunshine will suddenly decorate the wall behind you, the grip of your arm will be gone and a broad grin will appear on your partner's face accompanied by a tremendous sigh.

'Oh what a **RELIEF.** I thought for a moment that you were telling me that this injury was *serious*. You know, Alan, you *really shouldn't* tease me like this.

ON THE WARD

From Casualty, the usual hospital process will take its course and your partner will eventually be wheeled onto one of the wards.

If this is your *first* time, don't be surprised to find that you appear to be heading in a completely different direction to any of the other patients who were *not* wearing jods, helmets and hacking jackets.

Don't be surprised also, if the decorations on the walls which were the usual hospital dire warnings about all sorts of dreadful diseases and conditions, seem to be giving way to rather tasteful hunting and other equestrian scenes.

Nor, come to think of it, that the more usual hospital aroma – a mixture of carbolic and ether – seems to be taking on the more familiar pong of

MUCK

All will come clear as you turn a corridor corner and see up ahead the ward name which will be something like: ASHINGTON LAWRENCE RIDING CLUB PERPETUAL INJURIES CLINIC.

And as you enter the ward you will by now be gratified to see that each bed seems to be occupied by someone in your own state – a horsey person *in* the bed, leafing through the Horse and Hound or similar publication with just the one good hand [some of them who have been horsey for some years will, by now, through necessity, have perfected how to turn pages with their feet] and at the *side* of the bed will be the non-horsey one, looking like a distinct spare part, not daring to move in case required to do something like mucking out, but nevertheless totally ignored.

Around each bed will be the usual cards – though instead of good wishes from people, these will be from horses – 'Dodo Says, 'Come Home Soon Mum' and all that sort of thing. There will also be flowers, usually in the shape of horse shoes. On closer inspection you will find that in the main these have been sent by farriers, the cost being added to the next bill, or by vets, the cost being added to . . . well . . . the Running Farm Account.

As you walk down the line of beds, you will notice that several of them are unoccupied. Those of you who are fairly dyed in the wool in the ward will know that these are the reserved beds for regular occupants, and some may carry little plaques which announce that fact, like the 'Freddy Farquar Farquason Farquar Perpetual Treatment Bed' or the Di Ashington Smythe Suite' and above these will be well executed portraits of the pampered ones with names like 'Stinky' and 'Pongo', leering down from the wall with that smug self satisfied sadistic smile on their faces which can only come from the satisfaction of a job well done. Some of these beds may also be reserved on a group basis, such as 'The Lower Archbold Tuffington R C Position.' [come to think about it, I must *try* that one the next time the missus and me are . . . oh, never mind]

At the end of the ward will be the desk where all the nurses and other medics hang out. If you are well used to the drill, you will be well known to them and the odd jar of jam may change hands, Ward Sister Alice will probably consult you about a problem she's having with her Managed PEP and the Ward Admin bloke may keep his promise about the rose cuttings.

If this is your first time, then **don't ask dumb questions** of these people, such as: 'I suppose you deal with a lot of accident cases here?'

If you do, you will probably invite – in a very benign and patient way of course, because these are people who are so used to dealing with so many classically barmy people that they have developed their own tolerance of the human condition to a point almost equalling Job – a response along the lines of: ' . . . yes, we *do* tend to deal with a few . . .' followed by a rather tired look at the endless lines of broken legs, arms, crushed ribs, bandaged heads and walking wounded, displayed before them.

Only the mega stupid would then try to make conversation along the lines of: 'Horse riding seems to be a little bit on the dangerous side, doesn't it?'

But if you *are* inclined to such ridiculous levels of making conversation expect the swift and somewhat sharper response of: ' Well we certainly don't tend to deal with *quite* as many stamp collectors . . .'

THE OP

Some time after her initial banging up in the ASHINGTON LAWRENCE RIDING CLUB PERPETUAL INJURIES CLINIC, your partner will be wheeled down for a rendezvous with Clive Tombstone in Theatre.

If this is your first time, then **DON'T** believe anything they tell you about the length of time she will be in Theatre. You will probably be told that it will take 'about an hour' and armed with this sort of timescale, you will not doubt drag yourself away to some local hostelry for a hurried meal.

DON'T HURRY ANYTHING. Take your time. Find a swanky restaurant with entertainment if possible, and book at least seven courses – and to hell with the expense. On account of you know who, you may be, basically, well, *skint,* but this will be one of the few opportunities in your life of actually *enjoying* yourself, so it's worth little sacrifices elsewhere. Anyway you will *know* you are doing the right thing when you look around at the other tables, because you will perceive that they are all occupied by single men, looking distinctly relieved, even rather pleased with themselves and all appearing to be ordering the special which looks suspiciously like *'Cheval à la mode'* and downing it with an almost hysterical relish.

If you are a first timer and make the mistake of being still so strung up in your low grade Australian soap opera antics, that you rush things, just so that you can high tail it back to the ASHINGTON LAWRENCE RIDING CLUB PERPETUAL INJURIES CLINIC where you can perform your 'walking up and down in public display of your love loyalty and devotion' crap, no doubt coupled with the wringing hands, and the constant questions to the hard pressed medics behind the desk along the lines of ' . . . but *surely she must* be due back now. . . there's something wrong isn't there!!! FOR GOD'S SAKE TELL ME WHAT'S GOING ON ROUND HERE!!!! *I CAN'T STAND THIS ANY LONGER* all you will get is, maybe the odd ripple of applause at your performance [though not as much as they would have given that low grade Australian soap opera bloke who went through the same routine in 'Terror Teenage Lobsters from Outer Space' which was the only movie he ever appeared in back in 1957] from the remaining non-horsey other halves who have not as yet gone out for their feasting on 'Cheval à la mode' and the benign and patient ones taking you seriously in hand, rather like a lost waif and stray and telling you to go home with the rather enigmatic words:' . . . there's nothing you can do for her here, she's in **Clive's hands** now. . .' which will mean that all you will do is go back to a dark and empty home, musing all the while exactly what was meant by 'being in Clive's hands' and trying to interpret the benign and patient and yet somehow rather *knowing* looks over the faces of both the benign and patient ones, *and* come to think of it, all the other non-horsey types – and *worst of all,* prematurely bring you back to reality with a bump, because you will have been so full of the emotion of the event that you will have forgotten one extremely important question:

Q: While your partner is stuck in the ASHINGTON LAWRENCE RIDING CLUB PERPETUAL INJURIES CLINIC – *who* is going to look after Dodo and Poochie?

A: The answer, of course is:

Now, the first timers amongst you may erroneously think otherwise. After all, *you* are not into horses, are you. *You* are not barmy. *Surely* there must be sufficient barmy horsey people who know what looking after horses is all about to look after the day to day needs of Dodo and Poochie?

Not so. *They* are not there to look after the practicalities of all the hard work, toil and effort etc etc etc of looking after *someone else's* horses. They have enough pain, torture and sheer hell with their own, so why should they bother with this aspect of it?

What they will be around for, however is to **sympathise** with your partner while she is in hospital and when she comes out '. . . Helen, . . . oh Helen *darling* . . . I've only just heard the news . . . oh it's so terrible . . . but you seem to holding out so well . . . my God you're such a brave girl . . . er . . . you *will* be available for the Intermediate Get Knotted In Hand Out of Hand Gosh You've Got Big Hands Hand Trials next month, won't you?' and all that total insincere crap that people give to all patients: **pour scorn** on what *you* are doing . . . ' Jimmy seems to be *coping* but really a soul as *sensitive* as your Dodo really *needs someone* who *understands* horses, and young Poochie is really *pining* for his mummy . . . you know how it is Helen . . . these *non horsey other halves* . . . they really *don't understand* . . .' And of course they will be standing by in ever increasing numbers while you are trying your best to feed the two brutes with a whole theatre of criticism: 'Jimmy . . . oh Jimmy . . . you *don't* do it *that* way . . . look Camilla . . . **look** . . . he's **put garlic in the country mix on a 5 to 1 ratio** . . . ha ha ha ha ha ha ha ha . . . . have you mucked out this morning Jimmy? . . . do you **know** how to muck out??? . . . no . . . we thought not!!!! ha ha ha ha ha ha ha . . . hey . . . come and have a look at *this* you people . . . have you **ever** seen **anything** so **HILARIOUS** as Jimmy with a hay bale?????

I understand that prolonged convalescence can often lead to tickets being sold for the two shows a day which you will be giving to all the horsey types, so, like every Bi Skite: **be prepared.**

You will know if this is the case when you see something looking suspiciously like grandstand seating being erected around the peripheries of your field as well as a booth which looks distinctly like a mobile box office. Further confirmation will come from the fact that a steadily increasing number of people will seem to gather at the appointed hours of far too early in the morning and definitely far too late in the evening and guys will be parading up and down carrying piles of publications which remind you disturbingly of programmes. You may even detect that there is a price structure- with people who are wearing something out of the Oxfam shop seated in the prestigious front row [there may even be a velvet bedecked box, by the way], generally know-it-all types in most of the other seats, with a few people wearing the very best in designer outfits appearing to hover in the 'gods'.

You will also know if you are giving full value for money in the comedy stakes if they start applauding when you appear on the scene. In some extreme examples I have even known a 'warm up man' turn up and do a half hour session before you arrive, so that the crowd is in the right sort of mood.

Dodo and Poochie will, of course, be full value for money. Realising the situation from the first micro second you appear, Dodo will bite an affectionate piece out of your arse, then place his head in such a position behind you that the loving head butt from Poochie sends you flying over Dodo's neck and then somersaulting over his back before ending up, face down in a pile of . . . well, I guess you know what by now.

At such times you might even fall into philosophical mode – you know all that 'meaning of life' stuff. Here you are, in the middle of the night [this applies to both performances, by the way, but if you are a particular success in the entertainment stakes, you will now be enjoying the benefits of floodlighting] stuck in the middle of a field, being laughed at by a crowd of hundreds of horsey types, headbutted and kicked by two 'definitely got to go for glue' types, up to your neck in muck, cold, wet, miserable, and with nothing more to look forward to than yet another visit to the ASHINGTON LAWRENCE RIDING CLUB PERPETUAL INJURIES CLINIC where all your efforts will be systematically pulled apart by your partner . . . 'you *didn't* put water into the *country mix* . . . how many times have I told you that he has his country mix *dry* . . . you have to put the water into the *bran mash* . . . now you didn't forget to give Poochie his garlic? . . . Oh **FOR GOODNESS SAKE** Jimmy, do you **EVER** listen to **ANYTHING** I tell you????

At such a time, try to concentrate on the good things in life. Remember that only an hour or so before [if it is the evening performance] you were called 'Mr Squib' by a respectful group of people who regard you as someone called 'The Chief Operating Executive', or some other elevated title. Remember how you pushed a button on your telephone console and barked: 'Stephens . . . be in my office in five minutes or you're out on your ear . . .' and *lo and behold* you had the reply from someone calling himself 'The Sales Director': 'Yes, Mr Squib . . . right away.'

Remember how someone called 'The Group Chairman' telephoned you earlier to say something like 'Jimmy... I've just been reading your recommendations about the European Conglomerates you think we should be acquiring, and I couldn't agree more... I'm going to recommend to the inner sanctum that we take on board your proposals without any amendment and commit the 2.3 billion immediately...'

Keep these thoughts firmly in your mind. Take comfort from them, and remember that it definitely wasn't some self deluding dream. Such events actually did take place in the other world. The world of which *you* are a part. Where horses don't exist.

Remember these things as Dodo's back hoof so deftly kicks over the bucket of water, so that it soaks the bottom of your best suit which you are wearing because you literally ran out of time getting to the field before it finally went pitch black, and [to a roar of applause and side splitting laughter] Poochie strategically cow kicks a nice steaming pile of dung so that various large chunks of the fall out land on the front of the very shirt you were wearing that very morning when you received something called the 'Group Executive of the Decade Award' from the Queen.

Then turn to your hysterical audience and take your applause like a man.

THE HOME COMING

Sooner or later your partner will finally come home.

You, of course, will take a day off work to be the chauffeur and if you are used to it by now, you will no doubt remember to pack the extra pots of home made jam for anyone who missed out over the weeks you have been visiting.

Then, goodbyes and 'no doubt see you soons' having been said by all the medical staff, you will make your way home.

If you are a seasoned hospital visitor, then you will know that before you actually get home you will have to lay in a little detour to a certain field where two awaiting sadists are looking distinctly glum.

Looking at things from their point of view you can easily understand why. The appearance of your partner on the scene means that the run of nightly entertainment performances with matinees on Saturdays and Sundays is coming to an end, and they had rather got to like the smell of the greasepaint and the roar of the crowd.

It will also mean a dangerous possibility that sometime in the near future they will be ridden again- so that they will only have the flies and the state of the ground to bale them out.

Still, at least on this day, they can have one last twist of the knife in your flesh, because obviously you have not been looking after them at all properly, and just to underline this fact Dodo might conjure up the odd coughing fit to create consternation in your partner and the inevitable mention of: ' we'll have to get in the Vet *first thing* to look at that . . . Jimmy how *could you* let mummy's little boy suffer so *TERRIBLY???*'

Just take it like a man. There is absolutely no point in trying to suggest that the damn beast was right as rain when you checked him just before setting out for the hospital and this is nothing other than a cheap put up job. She won't be listening to anything you've got to say, because by now she will be examining hooves in minute detail, muttering 'I must get *Tony* in to get you some new shoes – I'll call him the moment I get back – he might suggest some special therapeutic shoes this time as they have suffered so much from such *dreadful* neglect' – and of course checking their coats and noting that they are both looking ' rather poor' but of course a few weeks on that incredibly expensive Argentinean Country Mix which added herbs and conditioning oils will solve that.

By now, she will be so full of contempt for your failure to maintain Dodo and Poochie in the five star Rolls Royce luxury that they have been so used to, that it might work a little in your favour, because she might not notice that amongst your other crass failings, you did not re-wallpaper the stable, nor that you forgot to turn on the air conditioning unit this morning, nor that you had failed to put the eider down rugs which she had specifically instructed you to put on the little boys last night.

Expect the chastisement to last for at least four hours. Expect also that your partner will receive a barrage of extremely funny anecdotes from all the know-it-all horsey people she telephones in the ritual phone calls, each of which will recall some hilarious moments from your floodlit performances, punctuated by the odd ' . . . he *didn't* ' . . . 'oh come on, no one's *that* stupid' . . . 'he did *what* during morning mucking out??? . . . and of course peels of laughter from your partner as she doubles up at some of the more hilarious episodes.

Then she may turn towards you with a rosy cheeked expression and beam a broad smile as she lovingly embraces you and says: 'Oh Jimmy, I *do* love Dodo *so much!!!*'

Then there will be the strings of visitors. News travels fast on the horsey jungle telegraph and your partner won't be at home for long before the first of the know-it-all horsey pals pushes you aside when you open the door without so much as a by-your-leave and heads partner-wards full of sympathies and injury comparisons, and of course, even more gags at your expense.

You will oblige by being today's dumb waiter, ensuring that this growing band of comedians is well fed and watered. Some you will know quite well. Others you might only recognise because they were in the grandstand for several of your performances.

As you move to and fro from the kitchen to the living room where your beloved is ensconced, lapping up the adulation of the masses, you may hear the odd reference to the operation and maybe even in unguarded moments you might hear your partner make reference to 'Clive's hands'.

Above the hubbub of tittle-tattle you might even catch the odd ' . . . ooo, he has such a *thoughtful* touch . . . . ooo it sent me into a *new world* when he touched me . . .'

DON'T EVEN BEGIN TO ASK ABOUT SUCH A CONVERSATION. If you do, then you only have yourself to blame when you face the ire of the hanging mob of know-it-alls and your partner who will profess to know nothing of 'what you are trying to suggest' and that ' Clive's a doctor and a *bloody good one* . . . he says I will be back in the saddle in a few weeks . . .'

Just suffer all of this in silence. It won't last for ever, after all. It will just *seem* that way. Then, once all the horsey fraternity have paid their respects, your partner will be up and about again, and by this time she will have relieved you of the duties of regular muckfrollicking and the twice daily ritual routines with Dodo and Poochie, so, thinking positively for a moment, things are **definitely beginning to go your way.**

So life's not really *that* bad, is it? And if the best comes to the best you may one day be allowed the odd bit of rumpy pumpy – as long as it takes place at some sort of sensible hour which doesn't conflict with horse activities – say, a five minute envelope after evening muckfrollicking and before the first of the ritual evening telephone calls. That should be sufficient

Anytime later than the last call of the evening will of course be impinging on bed time, and sleep is an important commodity when you have to get up at 4am to prepare for morning muckfrollicking – especially if the Vet and Farrier are expected, which of course they will be on most days.

So five minutes every other month or so, will keep you lively and *feeling appreciated.*

DON'T try it on saying that this sort of schedule is hardly sufficient to keep Peter in Perfect Performing Order and all that guff about 'Look, Helen, I'm a MAN and I want to *be* like a MAN and do all those MANLY things that MEN do . . .' It won't wash, and I'm sure that by now, having reached more or less the end of this little guide, you will be sufficiently aware of the enormity of what you're up against to even try.

DON'T try either the old one of moaning in your beer at the pub about how little you're getting. The chances are, if you are in non-horsey-other-halves type company that most of them will look at you with admiration saying things like: 'you mean you actually get *five minutes* every two months!!! God, you lucky bastard'. One of these might even say: 'You think *you* get a raw deal, *I* only get it on Christmas afternoon for two minutes as long as the ground is too hard for riding..'

However, you might feel that there could be some light at the end of the tunnel because, without going into all the 'birds and bees' stuff which is sufficiently dealt with in a million top shelf publications which people like you certainly wouldn't look at [OK, OK, we accept that the one you were caught reading by your boss in the motorway service area the other day was *purely and simply* a matter of broadening your own education. *Nothing* more than that. After all, *you* wouldn't read *disgusting* rubbish like *that* would you – but will you *just* take a look at the *tits on **that!!!***], you know that even a schedule of five minutes every two months can lead to the patter of tiny feet.

You will find out if there is to be a little addition to your family from a chance remark from one of the know-it-alls, along the lines of: 'Isn't it *just dreadful* for Helen . . . she will miss so *many* events over the next few months . . . I suppose she will have to give up a few hours before the big day, and she might not be able to get back into the saddle for a few hours afterwards . . . I only trust that Dodo and Poochie approve . . .'

On enquiring what on earth this person is dribbling on about, you will then find out, somewhat to your surprise, it has to be said, that you are about to become a father.

Rest assured by the way that Dodo and Poochie *have* already been informed and presumably approve, as it will provide another reason at least for a few hours for them not to be ridden. Your partner will have told them on day one, and you will only have been forgotten, because in the melee of telling the Vet, the Farrier, Freddy Farquason Farquar, all the know-it-all horsey types and getting the motorbike courier dispatched with the news to Mandy Horsefeed-Cheesecakes far away in Muck, you will have been overlooked – or it may be that she just hasn't got round to telling you, on account of the fact that so many needed to know first.

You might overlook this initially in your overwhelming feelings of satisfaction at the prospect of actually doing your bit for mankind, procreating the species and all that sort of stuff.

Enjoy these feeling while you can. After all, you can look forward to months at least of non-horseriding activities, can't you? The chance to start a family and *be* a family at last and do all those family things which families do, like going to the shops and watching television and having parties, and having money... and then there is the creeping thought that your partner might actually *like* family life and if the best comes to the very best, she might actually *prefer* family life to running around in muck.

Dream on ... sucker... dream on ....

Sometime in the middle of the pregnancy, you may once again find yourself musing in the vapid half lit atmosphere of a post prandial sitting room, gazing longingly over the adverts for toy train

sets, football boots, soccer star stickers etc etc when the voice you have come to know so well will sound from behind the paper in the quiet peacefulness.

'I'm so *glad* she's going to be a girl . . .'

As bubbles of hope and anticipation pop in abject disappointment around your mind, and suddenly little 'Jack' disappears from your dreams to be replaced by cunning 'Camilla', you venture, despairingly: 'How . . . do you . . . know?'

The voice, adopting a matter-of-fact tone will merely inform you: 'Had a scan this morning. She's definitely a girl . . . er . . . I thought *Camilla* . . . unless you really have any other ideas [which of course you *won't,* because after all, what on earth have *you* got to do with it?].

'Oh good,' you might pathetically plane, mentally putting away 'Railway Modeller' and reaching for 'Dolls for Doting Dads' and adding [liar] 'I've always wanted a little girl.'

'So have *I*,' the voice will emphatically underline in a tone of increasing enthusiasm.

'I just **CAN'T WAIT** to buy her her **FIRST PONY** . . .'

BABY'S FIRST WORD . . .

PONY!